How Stop the Downward
are touching and impac

Stop the Downward Spiral had me in tears right away as I felt Karen's pain. I could not put the book down until I read it all. The depth of her understanding of depression and how intricately intertwined it is with addiction is powerful. Her advice on helping a loved one will help so many provide the right kind of support. It was refreshing to hear how important it is to distinguish between enabling and providing love and support. I came to know Matty and his beautiful soul through Karen's eloquent writing. It is a deeply personal and authentic journey into the heart and mind of mother and son. There are no easy answers, but Karen has many helpful suggestions to help fight anxiety, depression, and stop the downward spiral. There is hope, and she reminds us of the promise that anything is possible if you have faith. *Stop the Downward Spiral* is a deep and touching story. I have struggled with depression and addiction, and reading it from the perspective of a mother—oh, my heart!

—Kristy LeRay, Author of
Messy Miracles

Stop the Downward Spiral contains Matty's message of hope. Knowing first-hand his love for helping others, I believe this book is an extraordinary gift to all. Matty had the biggest heart of anyone I knew. I was unaware of his struggles in life as he hid them well behind his gorgeous smile. I don't think Matty wanted to burden me with his troubles, knowing I had so many of my own. He always put others before himself; that's who he was. Matty helped me through my drug addiction and depression with his kindness and ability to make things better. He was very charming and cheeky at times and loved to make me laugh. He could never be OK knowing I was in pain and believed adventures and being outdoors in nature would help cure my sadness. He showed me the sky and the stars it held, told me to listen to the sound of rain to calm my panicked thoughts and smell the trees and the ocean to soothe my soul. He was a constant friend and believed in me when I couldn't. I will be eternally grateful.

—Abby Chivell

I have suffered from depression most of my life. My brother lost his battle with depression and died by suicide. I always thought that seeing the devastating effects that had on my family would make it impossible for me to go down that path. I was wrong. I've known Karen for over forty years, and when she heard about my struggle, she sent me something Matty wrote. I read it over and over again. Then, it hit me: I need to fight this with everything I had, just like this young man had. Even through the darkness, he could accept his struggle and still want to help others. So, I dragged myself out of bed and started to fight back. Every time I felt its grip dragging me back, I would read what Matty wrote. I'm now off all medication and have not had a depressive episode for ten months, a lifetime for me. You said it would be worth it if you helped just one person. Matty, you have done that; I thank you for saving my life. My heart breaks for your family and friends, but I will never forget.

—David

Stop the Downward Spiral immediately tugs at your heart-strings as it's difficult to imagine going through such a tragedy as the author experienced. However, she has managed to turn this into a book of hope and homage to her son Matty. Karen has offered a beacon of light for others in a dark place using the hard lessons she learned along with her son Matty. Using Matty's words, this book offers hope in the face of depression and anxiety, and it reminds us just how precious life and our loved ones really are. *Stop the Downward Spiral* is a book of hope for everyone and guides you on a journey of discovery through the midst of depression. It's time to renew your story with this wonderful book.

—Steven Aitchison, Author of
The Belief Principle

A beautiful blend of facts and feelings. In *Stop the Downward Spiral,* author and mum Karen Gibbs guides us on a journey no one wants to take, yet everyone is touched by. Her son's story will connect with your heart and soul through hurt and hope. Focused on educating and equipping, *Stop the Downward Spiral* shines the light into the darkness of depression and questions. Informing ourselves allows us to better relate to and recognize others in a new light. Grace is a powerful gift to give ourselves and one another.

—Daphne V. Smith, Truthteller,
Coach, Speaker, and Author of
What's Your Scarlet Letter?

There is nothing more powerful than the stories of life stitched together with unconditional love and deep loss. *Stop the Downward Spiral* is one such story—documenting a mother's love and a son's struggle with depression and anxiety. But more than that, it's a heart-wrenching read, knit with so much understanding and insight. This book also offers helpful hints that can only be forged through experience. A heartfelt story connects this writer to her readers with the honest retelling of her son's life and struggle. A story that gives hope through faith and offers connection in the knowledge that if this is your struggle or the struggle of someone you love, you are never alone.

—Kylie Mansfield Author of *Thaddeus Bix
and the Pirates of Pepperjack*

Being a mother myself, I can say there is nothing that rivals a mother's love, and Karen's love is poured all over this book, which resonates so deeply. Karen and her family have been there and back through the experience of losing Matty, and after getting to know Karen better and reading her story, I can say that the world is a little bit darker without Matty's light shining. I felt so touched by Matty and Karen's story in these pages, and I know they will help so many people. In the pages of this book, you will read about Karen's experience as a mother of a beautiful child struggling with anxiety, depression, and addiction. You will also learn what life was like for Matty as he struggled through this. And it all comes together with Karen's desire to create a powerful narrative from Matty's wisdom, creativity, life, and dreams. As someone who has lived with depression her entire life, I can say that reading this book was a great help to me. It was an emotional ride that really resonated and reminded me that there is so much more to live for. Matty's dream to help others was to take them on an adventure, and that adventure awaits you in these pages!

—Tina Morlock, Author of
Red Flag Conversations

STOP THE DOWNWARD SPIRAL

Everything the person in your life
who struggles with depression
wishes you knew.

KAREN GIBBS

Published by Author Academy Elite
PO Box 43, Powell, OH 43065
www.AuthorAcademyElite.com

Identifiers:
LCCN: 2021908489
ISBN: 978-1-64746-795-1 (paperback)
ISBN: 978-1-64746-796-8 (hardback)
ISBN: 978-1-64746-797-5 (ebook)

Available in paperback, hardback, e-book, and audiobook

All Scripture quotations, unless otherwise indicated, are taken from the Holy Bible, New International Version®, NIV®. Copyright © 1973, 1978, 1984 by Biblica, Inc.™ Used by permission of Zondervan. All rights reserved worldwide.

Any Internet addresses (websites, blogs, etc.) and telephone numbers printed in this book are offered as a resource. They are not intended in any way to be or imply an endorsement by Author Academy Elite, nor does Author Academy Elite vouch for the content of these sites and numbers for the life of this book.

Some names and identifying details have been changed to protect the privacy of individuals.

Dedication

For Matty: Your life taught me about compassion and love. Your loss has broken my heart but strengthened my endurance. By God's grace, we will be together again, for with Him, all things are possible. I love you to eternity,

Always your Mumma. xo

Acknowledgments

People come and go throughout our life, but some leave an unforgettable mark. Thinking about the kindness of others has genuinely emphasised what I've always believed. We can't judge people by what we see on the outside; there is a depth inside that we are privileged to see glimpses of in times of need. Of course, this works the opposite way too. Sometimes, we are shocked and hurt by others, but I've learned about boundaries in these preceding years, and I'm all the happier for it. I choose to focus on the good, and sometimes a small act of kindness changes everything.

We never really know what we mean to other people. They see us from the outside, while we know ourselves from the inside. To those who chose to look deeper, I thank you.

Since that awful day that completely changed my life, I look back, and it almost takes my breath away. The journey towards healing has been long with some unexpected and, quite frankly, devastating twists. Life happens to us all, and I am so thankful for those who left me better for crossing their path.

I want to acknowledge these outstanding individuals here.

Firstly, although their lives have taken them on their unique journeys, my adult children, Kylie, Daniel, Simon, and Matthew, will always mean everything to me. Matthew, my youngest, will remain in my heart until I take my last breath. I thank and praise God for blessing me with each of them, along with my precious grandchildren, whose births and lives have enriched mine. They inspire me daily.

To my sister Rena, my best friend and most significant support during these challenging years of my life, words cannot express my love and gratitude.

My mum, Eve, shows constant support and love as only a mother can. Even though the miles separate us, thank you for the love that is always present.

To Matt's friends who went above and beyond in support, your words and messages were heartfelt and appreciated; thank you!

Special thanks to Scott Cochrane, Abby Chivell, and Kerrie Bullock; you continue to be a fantastic support, and I consider you family.

Steven Aitchison stepped up immediately to keep my online message going on hearing of my loss.

Together with Iva Ursano, you showed me genuine kindness and care from across the oceans. The distance was no barrier—thank you both.

Many thanks to Diane Guyovich, Corny Boers, Merrill Clarke, Catherine Maxwell, Evelyn Oddy, Keyra Conlinn, Jill

Acknowledgments

Young, Garry Gibbs, Kylie Mansfield, Jesse Gibbs, Rachel Casno, Dawn Thomas-Cameron, Kerrie Bullock, Scott Cochrane and Robert Zacha for contributing to kickstart the publishing process. Your generous support is appreciated.

Debra Hayes, the first contact with my publishing company, encouraged and supported my story. Your belief inspired me to dream of the possibilities.

Your example, Kary Oberbrunner, has shown me there are indeed genuine people who live what they teach. Your compassion and love for others, your desire to ignite souls to become the best they can, and your belief in me have entirely changed my life. I believe God brought about the crossing of our paths. Heartfelt thanks, Kary, my friend, teacher, and publisher.

Faye Stoeffler Bryant took time out at my lowest point. Your words, "You are God's marvellous creation; He wants the best for you," sustained me and encouraged me to look deeper for answers.

Daphne V. Smith, my coach and friend, has shared wisdom and strength. Your words and example lifted me more than once when I felt crushed and heartbroken. Your heart of service to others will forever be a constant reminder that there is always good if we look for it.

Many thanks to Greg Tosi for believing in this message and helping to get it out to the world.

Kristy LeRay, I'm blessed to know you. You supported and encouraged me to believe I can make a difference. The journey is long, and your heartfelt encouragement is like a breath of fresh air.

Tina Marie Morlock, my friend and editor, you gave me incredible encouragement, believed in this message, and demonstrated self-sacrifice to make this book the best it could be.

In many ways, your kind heart reminds me of Matty's. Your compassion and empathy show the strong spirit of someone who has suffered; we need you and all these beautiful people in our lives more than ever. Your effort to bring this book to life went over the editor's job, and heartfelt thanks are not nearly enough. I'm grateful beyond words, and you will always hold a special place in my heart.

I've written these thanks in no particular order, really just in sequence of when our paths crossed. Each one has enriched my life and, therefore, the lives of my readers.

To the readers whose lives this book will enhance, thank you for spreading Matty's message. We are all in this, and together, we can make a change.

On that note, I'd like to share with you one way you can make a big difference in the lives of those in need of support.

If you choose, please consider going online, leaving a review enabling this book to reach more people to become a source of encouragement and support for all.

As always, from my heart to yours, Karen. xx

Dearest Reader

You are the reason I've written this book. Inextricably woven into the fabric of life, depression, loss, grief, and the associated downward spirals hold us back from thriving in our lives. All of us, at one time or another, will feel the sting. Whether we feel that sting ourselves or it's a loved one who suffers, we need to search for the hope and healing I share within these pages.

This book was challenging for me to write. My youngest son, Matthew, passed away suddenly while striving to reach his goal of supporting the many who suffer depression. His heart was to help friends and family of those who struggle develop a better understanding of their needs. It was his dream to live a fulfilled life and see others do the same. This is his story, and because you are a big part of his life and love, it is also your story.

As a grieving mother, I felt compelled to honour Matty's life by sharing his message with those he intended to help; his goal became my mission. He struggled with depression and extreme anxiety for many years, searched for answers, wrote his story, and planned to turn life into a more fulfilling adventure. His writing is full of raw emotion and pain, but for you, his words also contain a clear message of hope.

Loss comes in many forms, not only by death. Depression and the associated stigmas can isolate a person and drive them to seek comfort with habits that eventually render life unbearable. Matty's dearest wish was to help others avoid the downward spiral into this dark place.

This book contains facts about depression, anxiety, and the downward spiral, but it also addresses the myths that have rendered us helpless for years, along with practical solutions to change the outcome for those struggling.

Depression strikes anyone, anywhere; it is not a respecter of persons. Did you know that a high percentage of people who struggle with depression also experience symptoms of anxiety that seem to arrive like an unwelcome visitor without rhyme or reason? Due to the fear of stigmatisation, they often keep it hidden.

Unfortunately, society has long-held beliefs about the cause and effect of depression that have not kept up with the times due to which, depression has become the epidemic of the modern age.

Together, let's change that today.

May God bless you on your journey of healing.

Karen x

Contents

Part I:
Depression, Anxiety, and the Downward Spiral

Part 2: Changing Perspectives

Part 3: Embracing a Brighter Future

Do not be dismayed by the brokenness of the world. All things break. And all things can be mended. Not with time, as they say, but with intention. So go. Love intentionally, extravagantly, unconditionally. The broken world waits in darkness for the light that is you.

—L.R. Knost

Foreword

I understand the difficulty in finding answers for mental health issues, so I get why you've picked up this book. I struggled with depression for most of my life until I concluded, the first thing you need to do is give yourself grace.

Depression affects the whole family—not only the one who is struggling. Oftentimes, we are our own worst enemy, hard on ourselves or our loved ones who suffer. I understand why people don't want to be around us when we are in this frame of mind. How can we show love to others when we don't love ourselves? And how can others love us? Isolation and disconnection are the obstacles we need to overcome to begin healing.

For many years now, I've been in a good place. I've learned how to manage my depression successfully, but I know this is not the case for many people. Your journey of discovery and healing starts right here, right now—for yourself or for a loved one who struggles.

When I first met Karen Gibbs, she was a grieving mother with a much-needed message to share with the world. She wanted to use her pain as a platform to support others who struggled.

Fulfilling the dreams of her son, Matty, who helped those who battled with depression or anxiety, became Karen's mission. She felt a need to leave a lasting legacy for him by sharing his message with those in need, just as he intended.

I believe in her and her message, knowing first-hand the great need for it. At that time, none of us could have foreseen how our lives were about to change with the worldwide events of 2020 or how we would need this message more than ever. Today, depression and anxiety are sadly on the increase, but hope and help are at hand.

Matty's message is insightful and unique. His story takes us on an adventure providing answers that motivates us to keep going, even when we feel like giving up.

Using her son's words, along with her own experience, Karen delivers a powerful message within these chapters. This story is one of hope and healing for us all.

— Kary Oberbrunner, CEO of Igniting Souls
Publishing Agency, *Wall Street Journal* and
USA Today bestselling author.

Part I
DEPRESSION, ANXIETY, AND THE DOWNWARD SPIRAL

• • • | • • •

The Worst Day of Your Life

On a seemingly routine Thursday, in October 2015, my life changed forever. Nothing could, or would, ever feel the same again. Four years later to the day as I write to you, it still feels surreal.

BLISSFULLY UNAWARE

AT THE TIME, we lived on a hobby farm, raising chickens and growing veggies. It was a basic rented home on twenty acres of land comprising of the home, split into two living areas, and a small outside laundry under the canopy of a giant mango tree. This little building stood quite a distance from the dwelling, situated halfway up the long entrance driveway. At the far end of the home, we had a separate room we could only access by coming outside the living room door and walking along the path to the entrance door at the other end.

Mum was with me that day. She was doing a Bible study in the end room and had asked for my help. I was dividing my time between the kitchen where I was making a cheesecake and the end room where I would help Mum with her study. It was shaping up to be a good day, and I remember feeling content. We had only been home from Bible school in New South Wales for a few days; we were still buzzing with gratitude and felt so uplifted.

The sun was shining, birds were singing, and right outside my door in his lush green paddock, my horse was grazing contentedly. All was right with the world, or so I thought. It still strikes me as something amiss that I didn't have a warning or an inkling my world was about to come crashing down around me within a split second.

A BOLT FROM THE BLUE

On that fateful Thursday morning, I was walking across the grass, heading over to the laundry, when in the distance, I saw a police van turn in through our gate. Even then, I wasn't alarmed. I continued walking past the mango tree, the filtered sun causing shadows to dance across my path as I met the vehicle halfway up the driveway.

As one of the officers alighted, I said, "Can I help you?"

The officer answered, "I'm looking for Karen Gibbs."

"Yes, that's me," I said with a cheerful smile.

Still, no alarm bells sounded, nothing to warn me of what was about to come.

"I'm afraid I have some bad news," the officer continued.

Right then, something clicked inside me. My legs began to shake, my chest suddenly felt tight, and my throat constricted.

"Is there anyone here with you?" he continued.

Oh no, please, dear God, help me! In a flash, my mind played over scenes from movies where the conversation started like that. I knew what it meant. It couldn't be happening, not now, oh PLEASE! My mind screamed to God for help, because in that instant, my thoughts flew to Matty. I think I knew but couldn't accept, so I begged for a chance to make it not so. In my muddled thoughts, I felt if someone wasn't with me, then the officer couldn't tell me any bad news.

As my legs began to shake convulsively, I said, "It doesn't matter if someone is here. It's not Matty, is it?"

The officer moved toward me with outstretched hands and repeated, "Is someone here with you?"

I pulled away from his hands because I didn't need him. It was a mistake; everything would be OK.

I pointed up toward the house and said, "Yes, my mum is in there," then I raised my voice in urgency, "but please tell me it's not Matty!"

The officer replied, "Yes, I'm afraid it is. We found him this morning."

In my fear, my brain began to malfunction. My mind focused on these words: Found him, he wasn't lost, he's at his friend's house, it's not Matty, this is a huge mistake, is he hurt, WHAT? A million thoughts rushed through my brain, but I couldn't make sense of any of them.

In a failing voice, I shakily spoke, "He's OK, though . . . isn't he?"

"No, I'm afraid he's not," the officer replied as he reached out for me.

My shaking legs would hold me upright no longer. As my breath seemed to choke me, I heard an unearthly scream but was totally unaware it had come from me. I collapsed into the outstretched arms of the officer as he lifted me onto the back seat of the police van. The officers drove the rest of the distance to the end room, where I had previously pointed out my mum was. I remember feeling I was struggling to breathe, and I stumbled out of the van almost before it came to a standstill, making it inside with the two police officers close on my heels.

I looked at Mum.

She stood by the desk with one hand on her heart and the other hand over her mouth. Her eyes opened wide in a look of terror. Nothing seemed real.

I tried to speak, but my voice could not escape through my constricted throat, so I urgently whispered, "Matty died!"

THE EFFECT

Much later, Mum explained she had heard a shocking scream which caused the hairs on the back of her neck to rise as she froze in dread.

For me, the broken pieces of life began to explode unbearably within my head and chest until, almost instantly, my mind became blank, and a calmness descended upon me. I could not take it in. Looking back now, I realise my mind had shut down because it was quite simply too awful to comprehend.

Loved ones cannot possibly understand because it is tragically something you have to go through to know what your reaction will be. I had always said that I would die if I lost a child—die or lose my mind completely. Matty and I were so close, and I never dreamed such a thing could, or would, ever happen. When confronted with the situation, I shut down. I believe it to be a self-preservation reaction, not of my doing.

I lay on the bed in a world of my own, trying unsuccessfully to think, until I remembered the cheesecake. Sounds ridiculous, even to me, but I got up off the bed and went back to the kitchen to finish baking. That day, my behaviour taught me never to judge how people behave when faced with a shocking loss. You see, I couldn't just lie there. I had to move, but where could I go? What could I do? I was lost; I didn't know anything. I just wanted the day to be a bad dream, and I most certainly could not believe Matty was gone. It just was not possible. I tried to think, but my brain would not allow any thoughts. Part of me knew it was irrational, but I could not think past the first thought of finishing the cake, so I walked to the kitchen on autopilot. I think this must be how someone with early onset dementia must feel. I knew there was more I needed to think about, but my mind would not co-operate; it felt like a massive block was in my head.

I could see Mum hovering around me. She didn't know what to do and clearly expected a much different reaction from me. She came to the kitchen and nervously asked what I was doing. "Finishing the cheesecake," I replied. She hovered and asked if I should be lying down.

When the cake was in the fridge, I lay down on the couch. Looking back, I don't remember much about that afternoon—just a few bits and pieces. I felt the presence of God so strongly, and I know I would not have coped without my faith. It was as though I was a stranger looking in at my life. So strange and yet somehow comforting because I didn't have to face the tragedy of it all. Not then, anyway.

The unthinkable had happened to me, but for my mum, she had to face the fallout in her daughter. I understand she didn't know what would happen to me, and she felt fear. How strange life is.

Remaining curled up on the couch as people came and went, I listened as Mum made phone calls in a whispering voice. I was only vaguely aware my older son, Simon, was there, but the time frame got mixed up in my mind. It tricked me into thinking he had been there before I went to the kitchen, even while the police were still there. It seemed like hours had passed when I saw him, yet it could only have been a short time.

I bottled up my grief because it was too unbearable. If I could feel the full loss at that moment, I would not cope. It had to be understood very slowly. It took so much time, bit by bit with every receding wave, gaining more acceptance after it swamped me.

THE CROSSROADS OF LIFE

Previously, my youngest son, Matthew, had stayed at home for a month with a friend who needed a place to stay. Typically, Matty helped anyone in need if he possibly could. We were away travelling, so it was only the two boys, the horse, the chickens, and Matty's dog, Tippsy, at home. Matty had suffered from depression and debilitating anxiety for twelve years and had masked the problem with medication and alcohol, as is so familiar with many sufferers. He had reached a crossroad in life, and had begun to realise it was time to do something different.

With his personal knowledge of suffering and addiction, combined with his caring nature, Matty formed a mission to impart a vital message to as many people as possible. He also had a great idea to help five other depression sufferers while turning his life around. Matty felt he couldn't heal while so many others still suffered, so he was hopeful and excited to plan a fundraiser to help these other people. The first step was to get himself into rehab to remove the crutch of alcohol from his life. He was finally on track and set about preparing for this first step in his recovery. Matty needed some clothes and shoes for which he asked if I could lend him the money.

I was so happy to help, as I knew it would give him confidence and help with his self-esteem. I believe we should always reward the small steps and show as much support as possible. We had been messaging back and forth while he was detoxing. He was so excited to turn his life around and was joking about rehab.

One message I wrote: *Great, Matty! Only you can get your life back, so I hope you stay strong. I can't wait to hear about your camping/fishing/travelling stories in the future! xx*

He replied: *I can smell the marshmallows from here. There's no way I'm not doing this now. I'm just really tired—had my first few hours of sleep this morning.*

8

We texted back and forth, with me joking about rehab being like a holiday camp. He said he hadn't had anxiety for a week. I noticed the paperwork said they take seventeen- to twenty-nine-year-olds, so I mentioned how lucky he was to get accepted.

He replied: *Yeah, I know, but they said they take up to thirty-five depending on the case. BTW, thank you for helping me today. I looooove you soooo much. Finally, I'm ready to turn my life around. So excited! xx*

Knowing now that he was not to live much longer, I am so thankful I helped him. He did his best, and so did I. I feel so blessed I don't have to live with the regret of not supporting his efforts.

TREASURE THE MEMORIES

I hadn't seen Matty since I waved him off to rehab because I had been away babysitting. While rushing home to hug him before he left, I passed the van as Matty and his dad drove by on their way to the train station. In my mind's eye, I can still see him leaning forward, blowing me kisses as our vehicles passed. I'll treasure that sweet memory with all my heart as it turned out to be the last time I was to see my boy alive.

MATTHEW, MY SON

Matty came out of rehab earlier than expected and went down the coast to stay at the home of a friend for a short time. He felt very unwell within the first day of his stay. He couldn't sleep for days and suffered constant stomach pain which kept him home from work. Luckily, he had a very understanding boss to whom I will always be thankful.

Matty wasn't one to rush to the doctor as he felt they always said the same thing. I'm sure, had he known the seriousness of his condition, he would have called me. In his wildest dreams, he would never have thought these pains were symptomatic of an insidious problem capable of ending his life.

One of the problems with detox, rehab, and adding medications into the mix is that it also changes the tolerance within the body. We only got this information after Matty passed away. This needs to be discussed more, and loved ones made aware. Even the person dealing with it needs to be better informed. After detox and rehab, especially if new medications are taken, as was the case with Matty, the body and brain will not react the same to outside stimulations as it did before.

Matty had felt very claustrophobic in rehab. He wrote to me: *Nothing bad has happened, but I've checked out. I'm not going back to how things were. I've left because I need to move forward, and as much as I loved it and all my new friends, I need to move forward right now and go back to work. I was so claustrophobic in there. Don't be sad. I've learned so much, and good things are about to happen. x*

Sadly, his health didn't let him move on. He was in pain and couldn't sleep or work.

After Matty passed away, my eldest son, Daniel, traced back his last days using his phone messages and calls. His last message was to his boss. He wrote to thank him for understanding that he felt too ill to work and that he was wrong coming out of rehab early. He wrote: *I was wrong. They were right. I have to go back.* I'm sure that would have been the outcome had he not passed away that night in his sleep.

I know Matty would want to share this message too. When Daniel contacted rehab, they said this happens often. People think they are better; they leave rehab and don't make it. It has a lot to do with the adjustments in the body, especially if new medications are involved. I wish I had known this was a possible outcome so I could have done more, but to anyone who is in this position, I hope this helps you. Stay the course and listen to the professionals. Matty would want to help in any way he could. He would be the first to say it's not easy, but it must be done.

I feel that if parents or loved ones were made aware of this possible outcome, we could be better prepared. Not knowing feels like taking a huge chance, gambling with someone's very life. It gets back to support and clearly shows what a good support system can do for someone suffering. Anyone living through this trauma needs to have support, as they find themselves struggling with a set of different issues while feeling they are supposed to be better and should be coping.

There is no point in thinking about what if's. Grief leaves a hollowness, an ache in my chest that to this day has not left me. He is my baby, my youngest child, yet a man who I am so blessed to have mothered.

···2···
What Is Depression and Anxiety?

The Surprising Cause and Critical Forewarning

GOD'S PRESENCE

STRANGE HOW I vividly remember every detail of that day in October. It's as though someone etched it onto my brain, yet the following years became a blur. I felt as though I lived on a different level, suspended close to God, high above my old life. I wept, prayed continually from my heart because the words just wouldn't form, and I could take in very little for the next twenty months, either mentally or physically. I lost ten kilos during the first five weeks. I couldn't watch television, listen to music, or stimulate my brain. I would go through the motions every day, as though in a dream, staying close to God in prayerful thoughts. Everything became a painful reminder. My mind shut down from everyday life, and fog surrounded my brain, but I could feel God's presence like never before. He never left me and showed me many signs which saved my sanity.

Bit by bit, I began to feel the pain of grief. Each time it surfaced, my mind would shut down before it became too much to bear. As time went on, I could feel and accept more of the pain.

One particularly overwhelming day, I was doing the mundane task of clothes washing when suddenly I felt the grief erupt. As my stomach clenched, I looked up to the beautifully changing clouds floating across the bright blue sky. It looked so vast and so distant, and suddenly, the time and space seemed to overwhelm me. I wanted to reach those clouds, reach out to God, but I couldn't reach His dwelling place. It was too far, too impossible, too heart-breaking. I screamed like never before, calling Matthews' name over and over, louder and more insistent, as though somehow my voice would reach that vast space. I screamed and screamed his name until I could speak no more. That was a turning point. A release and overwhelming loss consumed me, then I felt the urge to write. I got pen and paper and poured out my heart to Matty and God. This writing has now become very dear to me. One piece became my statement of faith which is included at the end of this book. I have the piece in my Bible along with a beautiful drawing of Matty's.

I often think of something Matty wrote about his efforts to turn his life around, and I know it was his effort to live as God intended. "Love my mum, my dad, my brothers, Daniel and Simon, my sister, Kylie, and all their kids sooooo much. I spend most of my days trying to walk in their footsteps. As the youngest, I'm the most blessed. Thank you all for showing me the way and never giving up on me. God bless! xx"

This gives me comfort because we never gave up on him, and he never gave up on himself. Our Heavenly Father never gave up on him either. He, too, never turns from us, even in death, as long as we believe.

GRIEF AND UNTOLD LOVE

Although I stood in the darkest place I had ever been, this time allowed me to see and feel miracles in my life that words cannot describe. Free of life's pressures, it was only me with my Heavenly Father present. I could feel His arms around me, and I felt desperate to remain there.

The privilege of being in this place is one of the greatest blessings of my life and completely changed me for the better. He held me together with immeasurable love, more potent than the power of death. Ironically, the tragedy of losing my boy plummeted me into the depths of despair, where I learned was the best place to bond with God. It was the worst yet the best experience, bound together in grief and untold love. I have discovered that we, as humans, are capable of so much more. We fear and avoid trauma and pain, yet the most profound shock has the power to raise us into an authentic life with Christ. Some people need to learn this; others seem naturally attuned to this knowledge. Matty seemed to be of the latter. He knew.

Matty also believed that no pain was a waste. He sought to help others using the lessons learned during his struggles. In many ways, Matty was years ahead of me in the conscious knowledge of God's love. I realised he had already felt that closeness to God, while I, although having been a faithful follower for all of my life, had not truly felt the power of a loving conviction into which this trauma had catapulted me. Through Matty's death, I learned this lesson in a way I can never forget, and I know with all my heart the purpose was for Christ to further his work within me. I also know Matty is not lost. God used him for the greater good, and my faith assures me I will hold my boy again. In Matthew 21:22 (TLB), Jesus guarantees that *whatever I ask for in prayer will be received, if I only believe!* In Mark 9:21–23 (TLB), we read of a miracle which begins with a desperate father pleading with Jesus to heal his son: *"Oh, have mercy on us and do something if you can."*

Jesus asked: *"If I can? Anything is possible if you have faith."*

Human nature limits our ability to believe or understand the unlimited power of God, but faith is the key.

I realised that no matter what we have believed in the past, or what others try to tell us, there is only one real answer: faith. Having a close and meaningful relationship with God, not living our lives dictated to by the rules of men while mindlessly sitting in church every Sunday, is the only way we can find the peace as Jesus promised. I believe. It's that simple.

In Mark 5: 22–43 (TLB), the story of Jairus and his daughter brings home the incredible power of faith. The leader of the local synagogue came and fell before Jesus, pleading with Him to heal his little daughter. She was only twelve. *"She is at the point of death,* he said in desperation. *Please come and place your hands on her and make her live."*

The jostling crowds waylaid Jesus as He walked with Jairus. There was a woman in the group who was also desperate for healing. She believed if she could only touch Jesus, His power would heal her. Sure enough, the moment she touched Him, she knew she was well. Jesus felt the healing power go out from His body and asked who touched him. The woman fell at His feet and told Him what she had done. Jesus replied, *"Daughter, your faith has made you well; go in peace, healed of your disease."*

While this was going on, a messenger arrived from Jairus's home with the news that it was too late. His daughter had died, and there was no point in Jesus coming now. I feel this is a lack of faith. We need to ignore the naysayers and put our trust completely in our God. It is the only way forward. Jesus ignored the comments and said to Jairus: *"Don't be afraid. Just trust me."*

How beautiful is this small statement! Just trust me. Forget everything and everyone around us. Trust in Him alone. I find complete comfort in this! It brings me to tears. He will never let us down and never leave us. There is a hope that no one can take from us. We each have a unique relationship with our Heavenly Father, and He alone knows our heart and truly knows our needs. Look up, always.

Jesus arrived at Jairus's home, took the little girl by the hand, and raised her to life again.

These are also great examples of *"what we expect we will receive."* If we close our minds, ignore our faith, and give up, then we will receive nothing.

If the woman had not had faith, Jesus would have passed by, and she would have continued living with her illness. Faith in action is powerful, and God's love knows no bounds. I am at peace in that knowledge.

A HEART OF SERVICE

During that season of my life, a quote surfaced that gave me immense comfort and set me on the path of service to others. Hence, this book and the burning desire to finish what Matty started. I've woven my story into these pages, but you don't need to be a person of faith to benefit. My strength comes from God, but my desire to serve is for everyone.

The quote I refer to is 2nd Corinthians 1:3–5 (TLB):

What a wonderful God we have—He is the Father of our Lord Jesus Christ, the source of every mercy, and the one who so wonderfully comforts and strengthens us in our hardships and trials. And why does He do this? So that when others are troubled, needing our sympathy and encouragement, we can pass on to them this same help and comfort God has given us. You can be sure that the more we undergo sufferings for Christ, the more He will shower us with His comfort and encouragement.

As time went on, this quote played over in my mind, and I found ways to support others through the grief that comes from losing a child. God truly knows our needs. We are brought so close to our loving Heavenly Father by sharing our deepest and most painful emotions through prayer. He is our Father, full of love and compassion. He gives us a promise of a future free of the pain we suffer now. We can bear anything knowing He is near. How amazing it is to feel His presence and, through His love, become a comforting presence for others in need. I have a natural tendency to feel empathy and support others in need. The loss of my son is the hardest thing I've ever had to endure, and whenever I heard of other mums going through this, I could feel their pain in my heart. I often reached out to offer what comfort and support I could just to let them know they were not alone. This is part of the reason I created a group to support other women. It may seem a small thing, but when in turmoil and grief, the smallest act of kindness and compassion feels like a mountain of support. What an amazing God we have!

RECOLLECTIONS

When I think of the time before this devastating loss, I remember the years of struggle and the search for answers to Matty's depression. We understand best through experience. I remember everything Matty told me, but it has genuinely taken me this long to come to terms with this journey. Matty being missing from my life catapulted me into a season of grief and a depressed state of mind, which was to continue in many forms for several years. Previously, my mind was closed. Like most of us, I blindly believed the information available on depression and the associated downward spirals. I had to actually live through it to realise the folly of not following my gut.

During the years of Matty's struggle, I was a desperate mother who listened to doctors over and above my son's intuition and feelings. He knew what he needed, but it took me a lot longer to accept it. When I would push for him to go on medication, he would put his arm around me and lovingly say, *"Mumma, you just don't understand."* Since his passing, I have gathered and read all his writings, searched for answers, and found some mind-blowing research that backs up Matty's beliefs. How I could have been so naïve in the past I have no idea, but I believe God has put it on my heart to bring out the answers needed. I've learned to take my perspective out of the equation. We actually need to be open to God, open to seeking answers. A closed mind will not produce growth.

Matty had ideas that were very different from mainstream thoughts on what caused depression and anxiety and how to live a fulfilled life. I am so thankful to finally understand and share his message with you throughout this book.

A BATTLE OF ENDURANCE

I started writing not long after Matty's passing. Grief is a battle of endurance, but I felt as though I had work to do, together with my boy, to help anyone who suffered depression. That was the first part of Matty's mission. The second was to stop the downward spiral into drug or alcohol misuse, which all too often goes hand in hand with prolonged depression.

In one of the fundraising letters, Matty wrote, "If I can help even one person, then my suffering has not been in vain."

He felt deeply the pain of others and was passionate in doing everything he could to help.

After his passing, I was driven to make sure he hadn't suffered in vain and that others in need would hear his message, just as he intended.

GRIEF IS LOVE WITH NO PLACE TO GO

You see, I've learned that grief is love with no place to go, and it, too, needs an outlet to be a healthy part of living. So, I've focused my love for Matty into this book. Making a difference in the lives of those suffering from depression has fulfilled Matty's life dream, and in so doing has also given my heart a home. Through prayer and guidance from God, Matty's vision has come to life, his message shared. He would be ecstatic to realise his words reached those who needed them. Knowing this gives me immense comfort and hope for the future. I, too, have grown and developed throughout this process.

I began with a burning desire to share Matty's message, but moving on from there, I have realised my love for Matty, and the grief in my heart, will forever need an outlet. As long as I breathe, I will miss him from my life, and my love will always need a place to go. It has become a journey with many twists and turns. I have realised I cannot do what Matty accomplished, but there are things I can do to make a difference.

It has become my personal mission to support women, especially those who have a loved one who struggles with depression or extreme anxiety. I can relate to these women on such a deep level and know I have so much to offer. This gives my love a valuable and uplifting purpose, which in turn makes my grief mean something. Matty would approve on so many levels, and that is comforting too. I have developed a Facebook Group, Women's Circle of Hope and Healing, which goes hand in hand with this book. I would be honoured to have you join me there. My dream is to enhance one million lives through the ripple effect of connection and love. Together, we can succeed.

THERE IS ALWAYS HOPE

Matty believed depression was not a disease but rather a profound downer due to continual suffering endured in life. The misuse of drugs or alcohol often prolongs the misery, leading to a much worse state of being. Matty, like millions of other sufferers, had lived for many years with the results of this crippling mistake. But hope was something Matty never lost sight of. By the end of this book, you, too, will feel empowered and enlightened to take charge of healing without the long-term use of drugs or alcohol.

Matty often wrote, *"Hope is eternal,"* and for those of us who wish to support a loved one who is struggling, we, too, must embrace that hope. Witnessing such deep pain in a loved one is not easy. Being a constant source of company and strength to another takes wisdom. We may have ideas on helping, but that's one thing a person who feels depressed doesn't need. They need us to listen and to be present, witness their distress, without advice, unless asked. It's stepping into the shoes of the one struggling and seeing it from their perspective at that moment. They need to feel a safe, quiet connection. Being a silent witness is far better than offering advice that unintentionally causes deeper trauma.

We need to see the pain, witness its effect, and be present. Our quick advice cannot save another person. Asking questions that give your loved one a chance to express their needs and feelings, while listening, often provides a deep comfort level.

Matty knew how to give this type of support to others and always knew what to say in support. I believe he never spoke of how he helped others because he felt so low about himself. When people told him how much help he was to those who struggled, his depressed mindset kept him from believing it, so he felt he didn't deserve such praise.

This is why we can't try to bolster someone up by telling them how good they are when they don't feel good inside. Similarly, if we ask them to get up, get outside, and enjoy the beautiful day, they feel lacking somehow. Intellectually, they *know* the day is gorgeous, but they can't *feel* the beauty at that time. This giant chasm between their intellectual knowledge and their feelings causes a more profound sense of loss and disconnection. In effect, we are making a bad situation worse with all good intentions.

DEPRESSION

During my online research, I read some thought-provoking descriptions of depression which were remarkably similar to Matty's beliefs. Beyond Blue, a mental health organisation in Australia, states, "While we don't know the exact cause of depression, a number of things are often linked to its development. Depression usually results from a combination of recent events and other longer-term or personal factors, rather than one immediate issue or event."[1]

Through my personal experience and subsequent research, I have discovered depression is an understandable psychological reaction to loss and disconnection. For so many years, we have been led to believe depression is either *a chemical imbalance* or that we are *weak* and should *pull ourselves together.*

This type of thinking causes more harm than good as it produces stigma in others and takes control away from the sufferer. Negativity brings down the immune system, and the cells in our body react to everything our mind focuses on.

Depression generally develops when we suffer loss and strikes if there have been other continual stressors. This loss could be anything which has changed our life and was essential to us. It won't be the same for everyone. Usually, a stressful life event like the loss of a job, the end of a relationship, the death of someone close, or even illness experienced by ourselves or a loved one can trigger depression or extreme anxiety. This is especially true if we have been dealing with other long-term issues leading up to this event. I liken it to a build-up that becomes an overload. Our bodies are made up of systems, the brain being the most intricate of all. My daughter says that when she is greatly stressed, her head feels like a computer with too many tabs open. Files flashing and multiplying until, BOOM, there's a crash. A great analogy, and one it's best to avoid.

The best thing we can do for our loved ones who find themselves in this position is the listen to them—really listen without judgement. Hold the space for them to talk as they need. They will appreciate this more than you know. A good friend will listen. You may not understand why they feel the way they do, so you don't need to pretend you have all the answers. Try asking them how you can help or what they would like you to do. Offering moral support can be so comforting, especially if they are suffering with anxiety. Maintaining a strong connection is so important. Often, depression causes people to withdraw. Don't take this personally because this is the moment they need you more than ever, even if it seems the opposite. Even a loving text message can go a long way to improving their mental health.

GRIEF AND DEPRESSION

Interestingly, I found, grief produces the same physical symptoms as depression; however, doctors don't diagnose depression. They also don't prescribe antidepressants for grief because they say experiencing loss is an acceptable reason for feeling so bad.

"It is something you need to work through, although I don't know how you are still standing," my doctor said.

I began thinking about the many visits to doctors with Matty over the preceding years. They never once asked if he had suffered any loss, not once. I knew for a fact his depression had begun after experiencing a profound loss in his life. Understandably, I questioned, *"If our physical reactions to depression and grief were the same, perhaps a similar cause could be attributed?"* Loss!

Red flags kept going up in my mind's eye. It seemed to be standard procedure for doctors to ask a series of questions, and if the answers were in a specific range, then you were diagnosed with depression. Without hesitation, the doctor would then prescribe antidepressants. We are talking about potent brain-altering drugs. It was and still is unacceptable to me. If your loved one suffers depression or extreme anxiety, your first question should be "is there any apparent reason for this deep sadness?" As you talk it through, you will find there has been an acceptable reason and probably more than one. Communication is the first step, and it is essential to begin healing.

DEPRESSION MANIFESTED

Doctors will often diagnose depression if, for more than two weeks, certain symptoms are present. The American Psychiatric Association lists these symptoms on their website:[2]

- Feeling sad or having a depressed or low mood
- Loss of interest or pleasure in activities once enjoyed
- Changes in appetite—weight loss or gain unrelated to dieting
- Trouble sleeping or sleeping too much
- Loss of energy or increased fatigue
- Increase in noticeable physical activity (e.g., inability to sit still, pacing, handwringing) or slowed movements or speech
- Feeling worthless or guilty

23

- Difficulty thinking, concentrating or making decisions
- Thoughts of death or suicide

The last point on this list, which can be obtained from any doctor, is where I am in disagreement. Yes, suicidal ideation is usually a result of depression or extreme anxiety, but it should be in a class of its own. If your loved one is having these types of thoughts, then seek urgent help. I can't stress this enough. To see what I mean, look back on that list. The symptoms in the first eight points will be alleviated using many of the methods found in this book. It takes time, compassion, and love, but the last point is not something we can afford to take slowly. If depression is deep and prolonged, producing suicidal thoughts, then consider this very seriously. Put simply, suicide happens when the outward pressures of life are greater than the inward ability to cope in that moment. It may be a passing moment or go on for some time, but the fact remains that once it has happened, there is no going back. There is no time to *try to work through issues*, so don't delay. Due to stigma, sufferers will often hide these thoughts, which is why we must do things differently now!

WHAT IS ANXIETY?

Anxiety is often the first sign that things are not going well in our lives. But what is anxiety?

Firstly, it's important to note that some anxiety is normal and healthy. It keeps us safe from harm. We need to be cautious in some situations to ensure nothing wrong happens. Crossing a busy road, feeling frightened of the unknown, or experiencing illness can bring about anxiety. The world event of 2020 has also caused a sharp rise in the number of people diagnosed with anxiety and depression. Understanding is needed now more than ever.

Generalised anxiety disorder (GAD) could present with any combination of the following symptoms:[3]

- Feeling nervous, irritable, or on edge
- Having a sense of impending danger, panic, or doom
- Having an increased heart rate
- Hyperventilating (breathing rapidly, sweating, and trembling)
- Feeling weak or tired
- Difficulty concentrating
- Having trouble sleeping
- Experiencing gastrointestinal (GI) problems
- Avoiding certain situations so feelings of anxiety don't overwhelm
- Muscle tension
- Shortness of breath

Once these physical symptoms are present, it's tough to focus on reality. Mild chronic symptoms are challenging to live with and too exhausting. It often feels like someone has turned on a switch you can't turn off. You lose all sense of self with feelings of low self-esteem, loss of control, and confusion. Encouragement and support are so badly needed, now more than ever.

Anaïs Nin wrote, "We don't see things as they are, we see them as we are."[4]

Our brain works in such a way that it will believe what we tell it and look for ways to make it real. Quite literally, we start focussing on negativity to prove what we believe! There is more power in our thoughts than most give credit. The first thing your loved one will say is, "I can't" if you ask them to be more positive. They can't see the wood for the trees, as the old saying goes. I know how frustrating this is too! A series of open-ended questions or statements is a better way of tackling this frame of mind.

One of the most difficult things is to convince those who suffer they are worthwhile. Open ended questions cause them to think a bit deeper and perhaps realise they are being too hard on themselves.

Depression and anxiety tell these lies:

- You are not good enough.
- You are not in control.
- No one cares about you.
- You are weak.
- You have no future.

Sound familiar? The downward spiral appears in many forms. Understanding this is their mindset while forming your speech goes such a long way to improving their thought process.

For example, a conversation could go like this: You have a fantastic knowledge of the ocean and fishing that I love to hear. I know for a fact that others are amazed by your talent, so you might be being a bit hard on yourself. Could you list some ways to use this talent to begin a business that will support you and help others? I'll grab a pen and paper while you give it some thought.

I'm writing a pocketbook that will be of immense help for those struggling with depression, anxiety, and self-esteem issues. *Your Pocket Coach* has bite sized chunks of uplifting thoughts, statements, and questions with a space to write between each one. It's a great resource for your loved one to carry in their pocket or bag to refer to any time the need arises.

UNFOLDING ANSWERS

As you read on, the surprising answers you desperately need will unfold. I am more convinced than ever Matty had been right all along, and you must hear his urgent message because depression has become the epidemic of modern life.

···3···
Who's at Risk?

Depression Doesn't Discriminate.

*I am now the most miserable man living. If what I feel were
equally distributed to the whole human family, there would not
be one cheerful face on the earth. Whether I shall ever be better,
I cannot tell; I awfully forebode I shall not. To remain as I am
is impossible: I must die or be better, it appears to me.*
—Abraham Lincoln, "Letter to John Stuart"

THESE WORDS SHOW us the desperate feelings that can
be associated with depression. Lincoln wrote these words in a
letter after spending most of the month, January 1841, receiving treatment from his physician. At this point, it appears he
was at his lowest ebb and that perhaps the medication did
more harm than good. Modern psychiatrists and clinicians
agree that Abraham Lincoln had all the symptoms of *clinical
depression*. Both his parents were said to have similar traits.
Sad was a term used to describe his mother, and after she
died, nine-year-old Abraham was devastated. He may have
had a predisposition for depression, perhaps due to genetics,
or maybe it was a learned response. But his life's circumstances

also played a key role. His first significant breakdown came during some dark and potentially depressing weather, after the death of a woman who meant much to him.[5]

As mentioned, studies today show that depression usually strikes after a combination of a series of recent events, followed by other long-term issues or personal circumstances, and this appears to be the experience of Abraham Lincoln. We all have ongoing issues to deal with in life, so armed with this knowledge, we need to be very careful about how we face life's problems. Perhaps it's a good idea to go through each issue as it comes up, instead of bottling things with the idea of dealing with them later. Sometimes, *later* never comes. If ignored, it can develop into a more profound depression, capable of resulting in suicidal ideation.

Abraham Lincoln was known to talk about suicide. In stormy, dark weather, he would seek solitude by walking alone in the woods. His anxious neighbours would watch him closely for fear of an *accident* occurring. They feared for his mental health. This type of weather often appeared to be a trigger for Lincoln. The death of his dear friend devastated him, then facing gloomy weather so soon after the funeral proved to be the straw that broke the camel's back as it were. Lincoln sank into an intense depression.[6]

HOPE IN DEPRESSION

This man's accomplishments in life, however, are a testimony to the fact that being depressed does not have to mean you cannot live in a worthwhile manner. There is hope and much to contribute. Lincoln thrived in life, despite depression, but just because he carried it well didn't mean it wasn't heavy. His extreme sadness combined with his strength proved to be a powerful combination in his work. Due to his severe depression, he viewed life's events in a very different manner to others. His often-negative viewpoint enabled him to truly perceive a crisis, almost before it actually happened! Combined with his strength of mind, he could then push through to find solutions. This is one of the many things we know today that indicate he had a truly extraordinary mind. (If you want more insight on how the brain works in these ways, keep reading! I'll address this topic in Part Two, Chapter Three of this book.)

Lincoln managed his depression throughout his life and actually used it to fuel his fight to save a nation and make the world a better place. This shows true strength and tenacity, even in the face of adversity.[7]

STIGMA

Depression can strike anyone. It does not discriminate. I feel that many have a bit of a warped perspective about depression due to the stigma that surrounds it. Unintentionally, many tend to hold themselves a bit higher than sufferers. A lot of that has to do with how we describe depression. I tend to avoid the term *mentally ill* because this term tends to describe *the person* instead of *the condition*. There is a very important difference.

I often hear it said, "He is mentally ill" instead of "he has a mental illness." Or even better, "He is struggling with his mental wellness." Can you see the difference? We don't talk like this for other conditions; for example, if someone has cancer, we never say, "He is cancerous." Instead, we say, "He is suffering from cancer." This type of talk clearly shows the stigma surrounding our mental health. The sad part is, it could happen to us or someone we love. We need to work together to change this misconception. Depression is something that happens to us; it does not define who we are as a person.

It's also important to understand the terms we use to describe the problems of those who struggle. Using language that causes stigma can discourage people from seeking help, and that is the last thing we want. The general public and healthcare professionals must be respectful and use the correct terms, while the person who is struggling can use any term to refer to themselves. This is important for healing. Some who struggle prefer to use terms such as *alcoholic* or *drug abuser* because it keeps them on track to recovery not to sugar coat what's happening. Others feel humiliated by these terms, so it is wonderful that we can show respect for the position they find themselves in and do our utmost to support them towards healing.

Choosing our words carefully
can help stop the stigma

Using stigmatising language can lower self-esteem and discourage people from seeking help.

PERSON WITH THE SUBSTANCE USE DISORDER CAN SAY:	GENERAL PUBLIC, HEALTHCARE PROFESSIONALS MUST SAY:
• Addict • Drug Abuser • Alcoholic • User • Dirty/Clean	• Person with a substance use disorder (SUD) • Alcohol use disorder (AUD) • Misuse/Recovery • Negative/Positive Test

SENSITIVITY

Statistics show that people who suffer depression are more likely to be creative or sensitive by nature. Sensitivity is a gift and does not mean weakness as is often thought by those who don't possess it. There are many examples throughout history of creative souls who also struggled with their mental wellness. In recent years as the conversation surrounding mental health has grown, many artists and actors have told stories of their struggles. I'm sure you have read of or seen many stories in the media. One of Matty's favourite actors who comes to my mind is Jim Carrey, who recently opened up about his battle with depression.[8] Matty could imitate him so well; we would all be in stitches laughing, but at that time, we didn't realise he struggled with depression. When someone on the screen is funny and makes us so happy, it's always a shock for fans to hear that they feel depressed in real life. We often forget they are real people dealing with the same life issues as we are.

Like many others, Jim Carrey's struggle was ongoing until he found a way to manage the problem successfully. "At this point, I don't have depression. There is not an experience of depression. I had that for years, but now, when the rain comes, it rains, but it doesn't stay. It doesn't stay long enough to immerse me and drown me anymore."[9] This comment is a remarkable statement that makes me happy. It means that Jim Carrey has found a way to deal with his depression without becoming overwhelmed. We need to identify the problems and manage them well. Like Matty, Jim Carrey did not benefit from medication, but he found healing through acceptance, lifestyle, and perceptual changes.

Depression affects everyone differently, but being aware and actively looking for solutions with intent is a great place to start healing. Carrey said that the medicine prescribed for his depression made him feel like he was living in a "low level of despair," so he would prefer not to take any mind-altering drugs.[10] For him, the medications made him feel *just okay*, and his belief is that people need to be desperate to make a change. Carrey said he takes the vitamins Tyrosine and

Hydroxytryptophan.[11] I believe a healthy diet and vitamin supplements go a long way towards healing any ailments.

Jim Carrey likens the word *depressed* to *deep rest.* I love this thought process. I also believe that depression is our body telling us to step back, rest and reassess. Our perception of what is going on is significant. Like many successful people, Jim Carrey found that fame and fortune did not equate to happiness. We are born with everything we need to be happy, but we often forget what we have inside; instead, we put all our effort into searching for something else.

I recently shared an anonymous post to my Women's Circle group because I loved the wording. It mirrored my beliefs that people can thrive in all situations if they look at the positives that are found everywhere. It went something like this:

People diagnosed with DEPRESSION are usually smarter than average. They have a better perception of the world and see situations more realistically.

People diagnosed with ADHD thrive in disruptive situations and embrace adventure.

Those diagnosed with OCD have a higher level of determination, a naturally good memory, and are compelled to learn new things.

People diagnosed with BIPOLAR DISORDER have an intense creativity level, high capability in artistic endeavours, along with a great ability in observing.

The last one, I know to be true; people diagnosed with ANXIETY have high levels of empathy, are able to understand others pain and joy easier. They also understand things on a deeper level and have strong levels of intuition accuracy.

Okay, it doesn't feel good to deal with depression or anxiety, but did you ever think about viewing a diagnosis as a superpower? Maybe if our loved ones felt more acceptance, they could cope better. It makes you view the world differently, so instead of labelling people in a negative way, maybe we should be giving them a high five for all their positive attributes and what they uniquely contribute to this world. Understanding and connection are so important.

I have always believed that people who manage to get up and get on with their day while suffering depression or anxiety show a great strength of character and are often amongst the most influential people in the world. People who possess the gift of sensitivity are almost always caring people who add value to the lives of others. We need these people!

MYTHS SURROUNDING DEPRESSION

There has been so much research in recent years, which does away with the old school way of thinking. The term *chemical imbalance* is thrown around too loosely. In our modern society, it is widely taught and believed that sufferers of depression have an imbalance which taking a particular drug will fix. Not so. I recently read a fantastic book entitled *Lost Connections*, which blows open all the myths about anti-depressants as well as the accepted cause of depression. The author, Johann Hari, travelled the world to find answers. What he uncovered is mind-blowing. He backs up all his claims with scientific studies which are all referenced in the endnotes of his book. He states, "We have been systematically misinformed about what depression and anxiety are."[12] I was thrilled to read all this proof that backed up what we already knew. Thankfully,

I don't need to rewrite his book, but I would recommend it to anyone who finds it hard to let go of the myths many have believed all these years.

PHARMACEUTICAL DRUGS

Matty's doctors prescribed him antidepressants on quite a few occasions over the years, but he was not comfortable taking any of them. He would try because that's what doctors recommended, and because at the time, I also thought it was the right thing to do. He had many reactions: feeling empty inside; loss of sleep; and loss of his creativity, which was so important to him and affected him badly. I felt so confused because I wanted him to be well, but I also wanted him to function and create as he had always done in the past. He felt he was taken from one misery to another and would lovingly tell me I just didn't understand. He was right. I had no way of knowing what to do; he had better ideas but lacked the funds to put them into place.

The facts remain that pharmaceutical drugs have many unwanted side effects.[13] *Some* of these side effects include:

- Nausea
- Weight gain
- Diarrhoea
- Insomnia
- Sexual dysfunction
- Sleepiness
- Suicidal thoughts
- Difficulty breathing
- Depression

Generally speaking, well intentioned doctors will prescribe one to *try*, and if it doesn't work, they will *try* another.

Can you imagine the impact this has on the brain as well as the body? Even if they believed there was a chemical imbalance, how much more out of balance would the brain become after trying different drugs without any proof of what was needed? Is a chemical imbalance the cause of depression, *or* is depression the cause of a chemical imbalance?

THE COMPLEX BRAIN

The brain is by far the most complex organ of the human body, and research has not yet unfolded all of its complexities. Studies now show a direct link to the heart and the gut.[14] By design, the human body works perfectly in sync and is capable of correcting and healing when conditions are right. Of course, we tend to make it very hard for our bodies to function correctly because of the unnatural things we put into them. Scans on the brain of those who feel depressed, often show the biochemical levels within the brain at abnormal levels. These levels, however, rise during many varied and enjoyable activities, indicating it is the depression itself, causing the change in chemicals, not the other way around. Focussing only on the chemical balance is a huge mistake. We are living, breathing creatures with minds capable of great things. It's essential to take into account social, as well as psychological factors. More often, health-care professionals now use a model for treatment, called the *biopsychosocial model,* which examines the *chemical, social, and psychological aspects* of the patients' life. For a good outcome, it is essential to take into account the social and psychological factors as well as the chemical balance.[15] Our brain is no different from any other organ. Naturally occurring chemicals within the brain can become imbalanced, but this is not necessarily the cause of depression.

THE BAND-AID® EFFECT

The ideal would be for a qualified specialist to do thorough brain chemical testing, which I've heard is available in the USA but, according to my doctors, is not available here in Australia. Without testing, it is a guessing game as to which drug a sufferer should be taking anyway. Do they have low serotonin, or is it dopamine they need? Just like any other part of the body, things can go wrong in the brain. Once diagnosed, the better way to treat would surely be with whatever natural chemical shows to be lacking in the tests. This might correct the chemical levels, but the depression still needs to be worked on. Popping a pill to *try* to fix an unknown issue should immediately raise a red flag. It's the BAND-AID effect because you're covering the surface, but the wound can still fester beneath. The search for the cause of the depression is where to begin. Some people will always have a potential to fall into depression, so good management is essential. Things like exercise and certain types of music help. (More on this later in the book.) Others will discover the cause through support and therapy, but there is always a loss somewhere at the root, and this needs uncovering.

MENTAL STRENGTH

We should also realise it is reasonable to have ups and downs in life. Our bodies are well equipped to deal with this. If something goes wrong, by design, we begin to repair. There is a part of the brain, likened to a thermostat, called the limbic system, which controls mood and restores balance during and after the routine ups and downs of life. The limbic system is a circuit of nerves transmitting signals to each other via two chemicals, serotonin and noradrenaline. People with depression usually have a deficit of one or both of these chemicals. I was interested in reading a theory by Dr Tim Cantopher in his book, *Depressive Illness: The Curse of the Strong*, that suggests it is more likely to be people who possess mental strength who will ultimately suffer from depression. The reasoning is, when under stress, weak or lazy people will give in quickly.[16] Strong-minded, tenacious characters will push on and make more of an effort by fighting off any pressure to give up, therefore pushing the limbic system to breaking point. Depression would then, in reality, be a physical issue. Restoring the correct depleted chemicals with rest, diet, therapy, etc. would begin the healing process, but clearly, it is best not to push ourselves to these limits as healing takes time and rest. Perhaps depression is also a sign that we need to take some time out to rest our minds and allow our bodies to repair naturally.

UNITY

The modern society we now live in caters more to minority groups and is universally tolerant because it's believed we should all have equal rights; however, those who struggle with their mental health do not feel equal. They are struggling with the stigmas that society still holds, and they are trying to get through life one day at a time. By nature, humans crave connection, and feeling disconnected has caused depression and suicide to be at an all-time high. You would think that with all the so-called unity, we should be happier than ever. Not so because governments give the loudest voice to minority groups that many don't agree with. For fear of offending anyone, or causing disharmony, many others stay silent. Those struggling with depression and anxiety feel confused and frustrated by this but don't want to appear different. A basic human need is to belong, but, it's tough to belong to something if you don't believe in it. The state this world is falling into is cause for many to feel lost and for depression to set in.

I know Matty just wanted to fit in and feel a sense of belonging. He said that he needed to reach a point where he felt happy, could have dinner with a friend, and enjoy a drink just like everyone else without having issues with it or feeling the need to keep drinking.

Governments seek to "unify" the country. Still, I feel they could achieve this better if they honestly looked at individual needs, particularly the mental health of the community, rather than listening to the agendas of loud political groups. I once read an anonymous quote that really resonated with me: "When unity is the highest goal, then ultimate power goes to the most dysfunctional person." I think that speaks for itself when considering the state of this world. It's becoming more dysfunctional every day. We are all individuals with various strengths. Perhaps it's time we celebrated our strengths and understood that not everyone can achieve the same things. In this world where our children learn that everyone wins and there cannot be any losers, something had to give. Sadly, it seems to be our mental health. The stigma associated with mental health issues needs to end, and that would be the most powerful and unifying thing to happen in our society.

During my studies into *The Deeper Path* by Kary Oberbrunner, I had many lightbulb moments. The general gist of it is that at eighteen, we just want to fit in; at around forty, we decide we are fed up listening to everyone else, and we tend to want to break out and live life our way. By the time we reach our sixties, we realise that no one has been watching us anyway, and all this time we could have focused on our own growth and made a deeper impact on ourselves and others.[17] Straight away, I thought of Matty's wish "to fit in." My life has followed the same pattern Kary mentioned. It's as though we believe everyone is watching us and what we are doing, when in reality, no one cares what we are doing except as far as it has to do with their lives. I have been guilty of trying so hard to please others that I have failed to thrive myself. It was a powerful wake-up call.

Another incredible light-bulb moment was when my *The Deeper Path* coach, Daphne V. Smith said, "Even Jesus couldn't please everyone, and you are not Jesus, so why do you think you could do what even He couldn't?" Wow! This is such an obvious point, yet I never thought of it that way before. I have now learned to find a balance, and it feels amazing. Yes, I have a wish to support and serve others but not to the detriment of myself, and that *No* is a complete sentence. People with sensitive caring natures will always want to support others, but balance is imperative for continued good health, both mental and physical.

CREATIVITY AS A COPING STRATEGY

A description of depression that I read on the internet, written by Carlita Shaw, emphasised these points:

> People who suffer from depression are usually highly aware and sensitive folk. They are creatively gifted or perceptive in some way. As a result, they are people who find it difficult to feel normal in a society which places value on things that are leading humanity and the environment to destruction. People who suffer from depression often find it challenging to connect with others on a personal level. Mostly they are overwhelmed and disheartened by the amount of injustice, destruction, greed, cruelty and abuse that goes on in an increasingly hostile world.[18]

Wow, that's a powerful insight! These words held significant meaning for me because they instantly brought to mind conversations I'd had with my son Matty. He could not understand why people were so unkind to each other, repaid kindness with indifference, or didn't live in closer harmony to nature. Matty was highly intelligent and incredibly creative but struggled to fit into this society. He trusted everyone and would give away his last dollar if someone else needed it.

Matty would often draw or write to help him cope with the reality of life. He spoke to me often and said this is why he didn't want to be on antidepressants that stifled his creativity. Without his ability to get things down on paper, there seemed to be no purpose to life. In effect, the prescription to cure him made him feel devoid of purpose. A never-ending circle of loss. Matty tried to live his life openly but often felt disappointed by those in whom he believed. His life was not going to plan, and he thought he couldn't change it, so as a result, at the age of nineteen, depression hit hard. His creative talents were what got him through the day. When drawing, sketching, or writing, he felt free, but he was worn out at such a young age.

Do you notice any of these traits in your loved one who suffers? There is a common thread in the reactions of sufferers. Mary, the wife of Abraham Lincoln, once said she believed her husband to be too trusting. His melancholy tended to strike at times when he was betrayed or unsupported by those in whom he put his faith. It is written that when in the company of friends, Abraham Lincoln laughed and told jokes, but when alone, he dared not carry a knife in his pocket as mental depression often overwhelmed him. This behaviour is consistent with many who suffer.[19]

THE YEAR THAT WAS

Depression and anxiety have greatly increased this year since the world was sent into chaos by an unseen threat. 2020, the year that was. The whole world got hacked, and life as we knew it is not the same. The entire population has had to learn to adapt to a totally new way of life. We are restricted and cautious. Some countries or states have been affected far worse than others as the silent threat took hold unawares. We have, by pure need, had to band together to fight this insidious intruder. Still, because of the need to isolate, fear has taken hold of many. The use of drugs and alcohol has greatly increased as fearful people find they need something to lean on. The world has become a far more online place. In one sense, this has brought the world together but at the cost of human contact and connection. This is a recipe for disaster and depression. Just yesterday, a news report stated that Coles, one of our leading supermarkets, reported an overall rise in food purchases, but an even larger rise in alcohol purchases. In 2020 Coles reported a 10% rise in food purchases and a staggering 17.4% rise in alcohol purchases, boosted by an 80% growth in online sales. "This has been the greatest sales changer that anyone has ever seen," Mr Cain, from Coles Supermarkets, said. "When you have five million people locked in their homes or a panic attack across the whole country, that drives sales more than any other promotional event."[20]

In a study by the Black Dog Institute, concerns were raised at the number of people consuming excessive alcohol levels as a way of dealing with their anxiety during this difficult year. While 48.6% of those with prior history of mental health diagnoses/problems reported excessive drinking, 54.6% of people without prior mental health issues had also been drinking to excess.[21]

These are most worrying statistics.

CONTENTMENT AND HOPE

We need to find contentment, but manufacturers don't want us to be content, as it's bad for business. Think about that for a moment. Today, more than ever, we are bombarded with ads from all directions to buy this or that. It is continual and insidious. It breeds discontent. Talented marketers target our insecurities to induce us to buy their products. They work to make us feel we *must* have it. Consider the example of face creams or make-up. Highlighted in the ads is every so-called flaw. Do you have *crow's feet* or *laughter lines?* Then, you need this miracle cream to have smooth glowing skin. Of course, the models look flawless, so we are left feeling wanting and discontented with our appearance. Ads for new cars make us feel discontent with the one we have, and the list goes on. Most ads give us the impression that we don't belong; we are being left behind or lacking in some way. By design, these ads make us feel discontented, so we act to buy the product advertised. Contentment is not good for the economy, so our whole society gears up for discontentment. No wonder so many people develop low self-esteem, depression, anxiety, and eating disorders.

Change and awareness are needed to stop ourselves from being hacked. There is so much we can do to change the influences in our lives. We need to take back the control which in turn will build confidence and self-worth.

Social media and our use of smart phones is another example of how our brains are being hacked. We absolutely must question our own habits and remember that the mindful use of technology is the only way to use it. Some technical insiders have recently come out publicly to acknowledge that the companies responsible for programming our phones are working hard to get us all to feel the need to check in constantly. Chamath Palihapitiya, former vice president of user growth at Facebook admits to feeling "tremendous guilt" about his involvement in exploiting customer behaviour. This is why we see people everywhere, whether it be in cafes, restaurants or shopping centres, all staring intently at their phones. We are all victims of *brain hacking!*

Chamath Palihapitiya also says, "The short-term, dopamine-driven feedback loops that we have created are destroying how society works."[22] While this sounds almost impossible to believe, we must understand that many social media platforms leverage the same neural circuitry used by slot machines and cocaine to keep us using their products as much as possible. This is scientific fact and explains why we often feel a sense of panic if our phones are misplaced.

I'd go as far as to say if you or a loved one are suffering depression or anxiety, take a close look at social media and phone use and try to cut back. One small way to start is by deactivating notifications so the constant beep is not distracting. You can also disable the colour and instant-play videos that draw our attention. Perhaps you can come up with even more solutions for this insidious problem, but the fact remains it is totally important for our mental health to make these changes and more.

We also need to find something tangible to hope for and to hold on to so we can find comfort in the chaos, but drugs or alcohol are not the answer. It could be anything that brings us joy and hope. For me, it is my faith in God. Many of my favourite quotes are from the Bible. It has a message to instil hope and is the best-selling book for a reason.

I am not suggesting that people who read the Bible will not be depressed. My own years of suffering are testament to this. Depression does not discriminate, but having hope helps. I genuinely believe the Bible to be the best manual for life, as it brings us hope for the future. It's something tangible to hold onto.

So many times, I hear people quote the Bible without even knowing it. "We brought nothing into this world, and we certainly won't be taking anything out." How many times have you heard someone say that? The quote is from 1st Timothy 6:7, (NIVUK) but to read verse 7 in context, we should also read verse 6. *Godliness with contentment is great gain.* This is one of my favourite quotes. Being content and practising gratitude every day are excellent remedies for depression. It's a fantastic quote to live by, yet it's not what our society expects from us. Knowing this goes a long way in making better decisions and taking back the control of our brains to experience *Unhackability.* I found the internationally best-selling book

Unhackable by Kary Oberbrunner to be the best resource in accomplishing this. I loved it so much I now use it in all my teaching, including in a fun way for Women's Circle. Once learned, it's something that you can use for any set of life's problems.

BETTER UNDERSTANDING

The worst part of feeling we are lacking in some way is the terrible stigma attached to mental health issues. Firstly, we are being led from a young age into a decline in mental health, then we are targeted for suffering. Wow, that seems to make no sense at all! We need to replace these judgements with understanding and knowledge. With all the information readily available, we can now see how easily we are being led down that slippery path which ultimately leads to serious mental health issues. To begin to eliminate stigma, and armed with this knowledge and understanding that depression can strike anyone, we all need to talk more with empathy and understanding. Speak up if you hear people talk negatively regarding depression. We are often fearful of speaking out, which is natural, but opening conversations in a knowledgeable way will go a long way to stopping the stigma. In turn, this will save many lives and make life better for those who struggle or have loved ones who suffer. Confidently talking about these issues in a non-threatening way makes others feel comfortable to talk about it too. We need openness without judgement to best help and support.

On my vision board, I have written: Matty taught me to have compassion and help others without judgement. This was his greatest wish for those who struggle.

Depression presents in many forms, and due to the stigma attached, sufferers have become good at hiding it. Don't you think it's sad that sufferers of depression and anxiety feel a need to protect themselves from family and friends? We need to make this change, talk as openly about our mental health as we talk about our physical, and become better at understanding and listening.

IS DEPRESSION AN EPIDEMIC?

Modern medicine has come a long way, and it saves many lives, but it has also changed the way we look at mental health issues. The term clinical depression and mental illness has negative connotations for many. Previously, people were said to be melancholy or blue, which tended to sound softer, and there was no implication that they were ill or lacking in some way. Of course, there are many levels of depression; it has many faces and manifests itself differently in each person. The generalised depression and anxiety I focus on in this book makes up around 95% of all mental health issues, making this type of localised depression an epidemic. More than three quarters of Australians claim their mental health has worsened this past year since the outbreak.[23]

Today, the Premier of Queensland posted her intention to greatly increase mental health funding. Annastacia Palaszczuk MP stated:

> This global pandemic isn't just claiming lives around the world—it is taking a massive toll on mental health. I know it's putting enormous strain on families. We've also seen our elderly loved ones become more isolated and vulnerable. The Government will provide an additional $46.5 million for localised mental health community treatment and support services.[24]

This is an incredible amount of money for only one state in Australia. The overall support offered to Australians during the mental health crisis is 5.8 billion as of February 2021.[25] This shows the massive increase in people suffering a decline in mental wellness and it's a worldwide problem. In fact, the U.S Census Bureau recently reported that a third of Americans show signs of clinical depression and anxiety. These and other mental conditions are becoming amplified during the worldwide events of 2020, while affected patients and their families are also at high risk to develop depression and anxiety.

Maurizio Fava, psychiatrist-in-chief within the department of psychiatry at Massachusetts General Hospital, is not surprised by the correlation between mental health conditions and the events of 2020. "It is likely to cause significant stress and psychological distress for a large proportion of the population," he says, "and we know the rates are progressively increasing."[26]

The following chart shows the spike in reported symptoms of depression and anxiety from January 2019 until December 2020 in the US.[27]

Table 1: Used with permission under the Creative Commons License CC BY-ND 3.0, located at https://www.statista.com/chart/21878/ impact-of-coronavirus-pandemic-on-mental-health/.

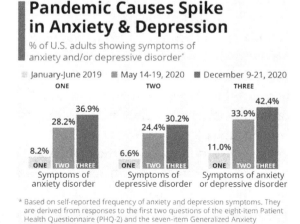

Pandemic Causes Spike in Anxiety & Depression

% of U.S. adults showing symptoms of anxiety and/or depressive disorder*

January-June 2019   May 14-19, 2020   December 9-21, 2020

Symptoms of anxiety disorder
- ONE: 8.2%
- TWO: 28.2%
- THREE: 36.9%

Symptoms of depressive disorder
- ONE: 6.6%
- TWO: 24.4%
- THREE: 30.2%

Symptoms of anxiety or depressive disorder
- ONE: 11.0%
- TWO: 33.9%
- THREE: 42.4%

* Based on self-reported frequency of anxiety and depression symptoms. They are derived from responses to the first two questions of the eight-item Patient Health Questionnaire (PHQ-2) and the seven-item Generalized Anxiety Disorder (GAD-2) scale.
Sources: CDC, NCHS, U.S. Census Bureau

statista

MELANCHOLY

We all have days where we feel blue or a bit down, and sometimes this can last for days. William Herndon once said of his law partner, Abraham Lincoln, that "his melancholy dripped from him as he walked." He was never a particularly cheerful person and often thought of as gloomy. Back in the 1800s, people accepted depression almost as a personality trait and the stigmas did not appear to be there with the force they are in today's society. In the case of Abraham Lincoln, his peers accepted his melancholy as part of his personality. He was not ostracised for it as perhaps he might be if he were alive today.[28] There is something to learn from that when we consider the life achievements of this man. Of course, we also know that people who suffered other types of mental health issues did not get off so kindly.

Melancholia has a history that reaches back to Hippocratic times. Its modern meaning was established based on Kraepelin's manic depressive illness. Depression is a deepened or prolonged sadness in everyday life, but melancholia has a distinct quality of mood that cannot be interpreted as severe depression. Today, the definition has greatly changed from that of the past.

Melancholia is sometimes called "endogenous depression," meaning "depression that comes from within." People with melancholia are likely to have a family history of mood issues, whereas other types of depression usually have an external cause. Social and psychological factors rarely contribute to melancholia.

Research suggests differences in the brain may be responsible for melancholia. Someone with melancholia may have less neurons connecting to their insula (the part of the brain responsible for attention). They may also have an altered hypothalamus, pituitary gland, or adrenal glands. These changes may affect a person's appetite, stress levels, and more.[29]

Back in Abraham Lincoln's time, not a lot was known about generalised depression or melancholy, so it was simply accepted as part of life. The increase in research over the years has produced so many conflicting ideas that many people shy away from even the mention of it. This closed attitude is responsible for much of the stigma in today's society. Over the years, so many ideas have been put forward as the cause that judgements have developed, especially in the older generation. The good news is that with openness and honesty in talking about these problems, the young people today are really stepping up the awareness, which is going a long way in stopping the stigma.

ASSUME NOTHING AND JUDGE LESS

We need to understand that depression is a general deep and prolonged sadness which will affect each person differently. There are no two people who exhibit the same symptoms. The difference can be confusing to those trying to help. If you have a loved one who suffers depression or anxiety, open communication is key. Even if there appears to be no reason for their low mood, delve deeper without judgement or blame. It's important to try to understand their feelings.

Some people who struggle with depression cannot get out of bed, while others get up and function quite well, at least on the outside. Others appear to have more bad days, while many hide it well. Staying in continual work is difficult for many, while others are fully functioning. Dietary patterns vary; while some sufferers use food as a comfort, others cannot eat and lose weight. Suicidal thoughts can be a dreadful side effect for many, but for others, it's not a thought. Choosing to take prescription medication is the path for some; others choose natural remedies; others none at all. This all points to the reality that depression varies in how it affects any one person at a given time. It can be completely invisible, but that doesn't mean it feels any less dreadful. Just because someone carries it well doesn't mean it isn't heavy. Depression is more than just a low mood; it is a dire condition that affects the physical and mental health of sufferers. Those struggling feel everything more intensely, so we all need to learn to assume nothing and judge less.

People who find themselves struggling with depression will usually have a fear of being judged, so they tend to hide symptoms. Those who are around them daily will definitely notice changes. Low moods are part of life, but if you notice changes that go on for some time, ask the question, "Are you OK?" Ask the question with intent, not only as a passing thought. This can make all the difference. Holding a space for them with love and time will go a long way in gaining their confidence. Really listening without judgement will greatly encourage them to open up. When you speak with your loved one, it's so important not to colour your speech with how you feel.

For example, if they are someone who usually likes to go swimming in the ocean, it is pointless to say, "What a great day for a swim! The water is calm. The sun is shining. What a day! You should go for a swim." That's how you feel looking out at the ocean. Your loved one will know on an intellectual level, it's a great day for a swim, but they don't feel that goodness. They feel bleak and don't understand why they feel so bad. The sooner the problem is acknowledged, the quicker solutions can be found, but you must let them tell you how they feel in their way.

Sometimes they may simply be feeling overtired, but your loved one may not understand if they are tired or if their symptoms are caused by something deeper. The difference between being tired and being depressed is easy to spot. Being tired is when you really want to go and do what you love but are too tired and feel sad you are missing out. Being depressed is not wanting to do what you usually love, tired or not. It's important to know the difference and keep an open mind.

UNDERSTANDING IS ESSENTIAL TO HEALING

We can see that depression is not what we believed it to be. If we can begin to understand our loved one who is suffering, then we have a great place to start healing. Many thrive in spite of depression, but for others, the struggle is real and constant.

This book's purpose is not to teach you everything there is to know about depression and anxiety; instead, I wanted to share Matty's story and what he believed to be the answer. I know how confusing it is because there are so many different ideas on this subject, and it can feel so overwhelming.

There are many reasons why people fall into depression. Looking beyond complex mental health conditions, which was my sole purpose for writing this book, I want to put a spotlight on the effect of generalised depression and severe anxiety, where on face value, there doesn't seem to be a particular reason for their suffering. I want to inspire you and your loved ones with practical-living ideas to help you deal with daily life while caring for someone suffering from depression or anxiety. Of course, the ideas also help sufferers and will put them on the road to recovery. Each case is different, so work out if you need a doctor's input or not. This book will help with understanding, no matter which path you travel.

••4•••
How Does Depression Impact Your Life?

Secret Sorrows

There is only one thing more exhausting than depression, and that is trying to pretend you are not.

—Jenny Lawson

DISCONNECTION

WE'VE ALL HEARD the stories. People who struggle with their mental health have been judged and ostracised for as long as I can remember. There is a vast difference between generalised anxiety or depression and extreme psychiatric conditions, yet they are put in the same category by the general population. Generalised anxiety, even if severe, and the sadness that comes from everyday problems is what the highest percentage of people diagnosed with depression are suffering. As we've seen in the examples from Lincoln's life, as well as Matty's experience, depression can happen to anyone at any time and has a considerable impact on everyday life. Often, the sadness can become so deep it feels more like the emotional equivalent of watching paint dry. There is an emptiness, a nothingness, a deep void that just is. It's that numbness that profoundly affects our ability to thrive in life. Our mental health, our mind, and our thoughts are what drives us to succeed and care for ourselves. Depression can produce feelings of disconnection, and this is where the downward spiral truly begins.

When someone feels disconnected, their thought process changes dramatically. It's easy for them to hide if we are too busy in our lives to really notice. This is why it often appears to be a sudden shock when you realise how unwell your loved one is, but in fact, it has often been a gradual decline for some time.

SECRET SORROWS

Those who walk in the darkness of impending depression feel more and love harder. They learn to appreciate everything that shines, and they live with a deeper intent. Their passion often adds to the stigma and can seem strange to those who live on a shallower level. It's one of the things on which we all need to develop a better understanding. It's a lot like a person who beats cancer or survives an accident that should have killed them. The experience produces a much deeper meaning to life and changes perspectives. Those who suffer from depression can seem to be intense and deep at times, and the opposite can also be accurate when their pain presents as a quiet, inward intent. Each person's personality will dictate how they react and cope with life. We all have unique strengths, and quite often, what first appears as a weakness can be a strength. For example, if a person has great empathy, they are often shamed and seen as *too sensitive,* yet people with compassion and empathy contribute so much to this world.

There is a profound quote by Henry Wadsworth Longfellow, *"Every man has his secret sorrows which the world knows not; and often times we call a man cold when he is only sad."* I love this particular quote because I can relate to it in my life.

For many years, I have been saddened at the judgement I felt. I am an introvert and a very private person and have suffered inwardly more in this life than I care to say. When the pressures of life threaten to overtake or when treated poorly by others, I retreat quietly to heal. Others view this as me being uncaring, holding a grudge, or merely being a miserable person. At this point in my life, I have learned it's not important what others think as I continue supporting others and take time out as I need it. It has taken me many years to reach this point. I am very thankful for these life lessons, because through them, my compassion and empathy have greatly developed, and I am much better able to look outside of myself.

However, many sufferers, especially young people without a lot of life experience, do not understand this type of harsh treatment. Their confusion causes a further retreat which often leads to disconnection from loved ones.

You need to understand the personality of your loved one who suffers depression or anxiety, as well as working out if they have a reason for their sadness. Things are often not as they seem. The old saying, "Believe none of what you hear and half of what you see," comes to mind.

CONNECTION IS KEY

At face value, disconnection may not seem to be much of a problem to you. When dealing with a loved one who suffers, you can feel exhausted at times, so when they retreat and all is quiet, you could believe that the depression or anxiety is improving. Things seem ok; there's time for yourself to go about the day's tasks. Don't be lulled into this false sense of security. I know how hard it is to deal with every day, and I know that feeling of needing a rest, but this is the exact moment that can make or break the outcome. Make it a daily practise to ask your loved one if they are ok. It never hurts to show you care, and this can break the awkwardness and initiate further conversation.

THE DOWNWARD SPIRAL

When someone retreats into themselves, it produces low self-esteem. It is an insidious spiral. Chemicals in the brain are changing in response to the low mood, attitudes are in decline, and as time goes on, the person feels incapable of change, incapable of doing anything about their current circumstance. Meanwhile, you, the person who cares, thinks they have improved because things seem calm and quiet. Remember the person suffering through depression, anxiety, mood changes, and family upsets does not want to feel that way. No one chooses to live an unhappy existence, but the changes creep up so slowly that, without awareness, there's no real chance to stop it. It's so important to be aware of the changes without becoming angry with the sufferer.

DIFFERENTLY ABLED

It's always so easy to look back at things with hindsight. The trick is not to let things get too far out of hand. Once disconnection is present, the downward spiral can be swift. Sufferers who feel isolated and disconnected can slip into a more profound depression or worse, into addiction. Humans are deliberately designed to need company and companionship.

Significantly highlighted with the world health issues of 2020 was the need for contact with others.

Within days of people happily ringing in the New Year of 2020, the most significant change descended upon us all. Fear gripped the world, and no one knew where this would lead. Whole nations were put into lockdown as leaders struggled to understand the hidden enemy and how to contain it. Those who lived alone struggled. Many others who lived with their families also fell into depression. Life was different: there was a hidden enemy, and being suddenly thrust into the company of others 24/7 was a far cry from their former life. Depression and anxiety grew ten-fold in the community. More and more people called helplines, and the help centres were stretched beyond capacity. The decline began. We had to question whether it was acceptable to feel down when so much chaos was happening around us.

People felt distressed and experienced mental health issues, but who gets to decide how we are supposed to process our emotions? After all, none of us had ever faced this feeling before. The general belief that the people with depression or anxiety are too weak to pull themselves together has led to many looking down upon sufferers and strengthened the associated stigmas. Those who struggle are not weak, just differently abled. Even Abraham Lincoln once, when feeling down, sat with his head in his hands and said he was *feeling unwell*. This is quite a common expression from sufferers of depression as it is readily accepted and doesn't need extra explanations. I use this very expression myself when I feel overwhelmed.

Depression is not who a person is, but rather it is something they have. Depression does not define them. There is no fault and no blame. Our bodies are incredibly good at healing when the conditions are right. Suppose we develop diabetes, high blood pressure, or have an accident and break a limb: we do what it takes to heal. Treating depression or anxiety is no different. We need to do what it takes. The point remains that it is not the fault of the sufferer. Depression is not treated or cured like any of these ailments, so we should not even say that sufferers are *ill*. I see it as a temporary state of mind and will take some time to work through. It goes on longer in some people than in others, but the treatment is the same and understanding is crucial. Perhaps it could be said that the sufferer is having issues with their mental health. Whatever we call it, the main point is not to be derogatory when we speak of anyone who is suffering because depression is a normal reaction to outside pressures or stressors in this world. It's how we learn to overcome that's important. There is always a reason, and in my experience, sufferers are amongst the most influential and compassionate souls I know. Depression is both a blessing and a curse. Labelling sufferers in a negative fashion will only add to their anguish and cause them to retreat further.

In recent years doctors have come to understand so much better how depression affects lives.

I think of those dealing with depression as *differently abled*. They are not disabled as someone in a wheelchair, for example, but coping with depression is undoubtedly challenging, and there are many times a person will be incapacitated because it is exhausting to live with any mental health issue.

EXTERNAL PRESSURE

Over the years, we have heard many conflicting stories about how to deal with depression, anxiety and substance abuse. Where does the truth lie? Many people belittle the symptoms and feel the need to add their words of wisdom, which in truth rarely contains any wisdom. I've heard everything from taking laxatives every day to clear yourself out because that fixes everything, to just get up and get out, and the depression will go away. Almost as though you can take depression for a walk outside and leave it there.

One thing I feel for sure is that depression comes about from outside pressures and not from something missing inside ourselves. Those who suffer depression are generally caring people who take life very seriously. It's critical to understand this if we want to help those suffering.

The original reason for the depression will be some sadness, accident, grief, trauma, or the like. In other words, depression has a cause. There is a valid reason for it, and this will go on as long as need be. It's not for us to decide when another should be over it or when they should have moved past it. Comments like *pull yourself together* are not helpful in the least, yet it is often the first thing said.

A DEEP SADNESS

Mental health issues have been with us forever, and why not? Isn't it a natural part of life to have ups and downs? Sometimes those downs become deeper, are more intense, and last longer, especially if there is no immediate remedy for the problem.

So much has been written or said that the cause of depression is a chemical imbalance of the brain. I am not a doctor, but it seems logical to me that if this was the case, then prescribed anti-depressants should fix the imbalance. Still, all too often we find that the condition goes on until the external pressures disappear, or enough time passes to make those pressures more bearable. I am not saying that medications don't help in other mental health conditions, but I feel we need to look at the bigger picture when dealing with generalised depression. The chemicals in the brain become unbalanced when depression goes on long term, but I don't believe it is the imbalance that causes distress in the first place.

Brain chemicals actually deplete as our mood lowers. Sufferers become psychologically imbalanced in their thoughts and feelings, and a deep sadness ensues. Research has been done that shows this to be true. Brain scans performed before and during stimulating activity showed depleted chemical levels, which greatly increased when doing something the person enjoyed. (I go into this more in chapter five, "Brain Chemicals.")

THE MYTH

The myth that someone suffering a low point with their mental health is mentally *ill* and that medication can fix *the illness* is the first thing we need to rethink. It is indeed a lack of understanding to think this way. Although we don't mean it to be so, this thought process is what causes the stigma attached to depression and anxiety. It also causes intense confusion in the mind of the sufferer. If they are on medication, they can't understand why they are still feeling down and are mentally and physically exhausted, why the imbalance in their brain hasn't returned to normal. They question why they are still *mentally ill*. The truth is they were never *ill* in the first place. Depression is a very normal reaction to long-term sadness or pain. Curing it does not happen by taking a course of tablets, unlike other illnesses we might develop.

The cure sufferers need is extra care, extra love, and extra kindness, but because much of the world don't understand, they often receive unintentional harshness. Do we believe we need to get them to stand on their own two feet, to pull themselves together? It is truly astounding that we will push sufferers beyond their ability. They are struggling to cope with life and are differently abled while going through this period. That is important to understand. Even though they are not disabled—like the example I mentioned earlier of someone who uses a wheelchair—they cannot live their life as usual during the bouts of depression and anxiety. Life becomes tough. Sometimes it's so severe that sufferers feel unable to live it.

ENABLING?

If we have a loved one who breaks a leg or develops a severe physical illness like cancer, we are falling over ourselves to help. So why is it when someone is suffering a severe bout of depression, and it affects that person so they cannot get out of bed, we are told not to enable them? Oh, I'm not too fond of that term. We have come to a point in society where we would ultimately push sufferers away instead of offering our help. This gives a contradictory message: firstly, they receive the message that they are ill and need to pop a pill, then they are treated as though they imagined the whole thing. To assume a person experiencing depression can flick a switch to resume a life we deem normal is quite possibly the greatest myth of all. Showing compassion and doing whatever it takes to get them through the day is far from enabling. Realising depression and anxiety are severe conditions that require compassion and love to help the person through, no matter how long that takes, is the first step in removing the stigma. Depression is an often severe and debilitating psychological and physical reaction to an event or events suffered by the individual. It is not for us to judge that reaction. To judge or decide if someone deserves something is not our place. We are called to lift the fallen and comfort the broken.

SELF-STIGMA

During a time of prolonged depression, sufferers often develop anxiety caused by the judgement of others and the judgement of self. They feel confusion about the long-term effects of the condition they find themselves in and begin to internalise the attitudes of those close to them. This is self-stigma. They will suffer numerous consequences as a direct result of this. By this stage they have, in effect, *lost themselves*. It is so important to support our loved ones and by so doing not allow it to reach this level of decline.

Lack of vitamins can also contribute to anxiety. Often sufferers cannot eat or do not eat a healthy diet due to their mental state. Instead of choosing something that could make them feel better, they opt for something quick and easy because their brain is too busy focussing on the depression to carry out the small task of cooking a healthy meal.

All of these issues cause a further break down in physical health, and if the sufferer is left unsupported, where would it end?

···5···
What Could Happen If We Ignore the Symptoms?

Matty's Mission

What you deny or ignore, you delay. What you accept and face, you conquer.
—Robert Tew

THE BEGINNING OF THE END

TO IGNORE THE fact that your loved one is facing a debilitating event, to believe the depression isn't real, or to trust in antidepressants to fix the problem spells the beginning of the end. Ignoring or delaying active intervention is so serious because the next step is often the slippery slide downwards into a substance use disorder or other habit-forming behaviours equally as frightening.

Feeling unheard, belittled, or that the symptoms are fake can only lead to some awful consequences. Lifeline defines these and more as reasons why many fall into self-harm.[30]

Cutting, anorexia and suicidal ideation—to name a few—can result when overwhelmed. We need to remember our loved one is already under immense pressure. Think logically: why would anyone want to fake these insidious symptoms? It is not a happy place to be, and no one wants to live that way.

Cutting is a coping mechanism and is an outlet when emotional pain feels unbearable. It is also often used as a method to feel something—anything rather than numbness. It gives the sufferer a feeling of being alive when they struggle to feel anything in their life. Things we need to remember:

- Physical pain can take away emotional distress, and it can create a sense of ease. It can become addictive when experiencing constant mental anguish, because eventually, the brain connects the relief with the cutting, creating an intense craving that many find hard to resist.

- Those who cut tend to be their own harshest critics. Low self-esteem is common, so we can be a huge help here with our love and belief in the person.

- Severe depression often makes people feel numb and crave to feel something.

When depression is invalidated, the person struggling cannot understand why they feel so bad. They are at risk of turning to cutting as an acceptable way to feel pain. If they are told they shouldn't feel this way emotionally, they let out the pain physically.

We can actually drive our loved ones to further harm by our lack of understanding. It is so important to believe in them and show love and care.

MATTY'S MISSION

The second part of Matty's mission was to educate others using the evidence of his own mistakes in the hope of stopping this life-consuming downward spiral. He was passionate to spread this message. We need to stop the stigma and openly reach out to communicate with those suffering from depression or anxiety.

Like cutting, many who suffer from depression find themselves dependent on alcohol, because once the sufferer retreats and isolates themselves, it is far too easy for them to look for something to help ease their mental anguish. We all know how dependency works: one glass of wine turns into two. That might be fine for a while, but then they need three, and before long, it's a whole bottle or two. Alcohol is not the only problem either.

EMOTIONAL EFFECTS OF ALCOHOL MISUSE

Excessive use of alcohol produces a deep-seated emotional effect on many users. Millions of people across the world, including adolescents, have developed alcohol use disorder (AUD). Characterised by compulsive alcohol use along with a prolonged depressed state of mind, AUD is an unwanted and debilitating condition.

Widely embraced is the habit of social drinking, but keeping within the recommended amounts is laughed at by many. So accepted is alcohol consumption within our society that many users don't take the dangers seriously. It is often the first choice of comfort for those struggling with depression, due to its ease in obtaining. Alcohol use also brings about a sense of bonding, which is desirable for those feeling isolated. These are immediate dangers. The long-term effects of being caught in its trap are far more sinister. Alcohol misuse catches many unawares as it's perceived to be a great refreshment, socially accepted, and just a bit of fun. Creative marketers target the very young with alcoholic beverages which seem more like cordial, thereby encouraging kids to drink long before their developing brains have reached full potential. The tragedy of this is our kids are not getting the chance to excel. Their brains are being hacked from a young age to conform to an unproductive and potentially life-threatening lifestyle.

HOW ALCOHOL MAKES A PERSON FEEL

Many don't understand how it can be a depressant when it's so enjoyable to drink. While alcohol consumption prompts the brain to release endorphins, its use produces many negative emotions as well. People report feeling a range of emotions from happiness to anxiety, disgust, and even fear. In one study, some even reported suicidal tendencies whilst drinking.[31] Yet the common idea is to drink more to block out these unwanted emotions. There is also the fact that to be a non-drinker is socially unacceptable, and no one likes being left out or isolated. Teenagers, in particular, feel this persuasion keenly, which is one of the dangers of peer pressure in the very young.

Alcohol drives our bodies to create an increased amount of endorphins, as well as serotonin, which are both responsible for regulating our emotions and our sense of calmness and joy. This sense of relaxation is the ultimate goal for many who drink. Still, the more often you drink, the more vulnerable your brain becomes to the effects of alcohol, potentially making your moods more unstable over time.

Matty wanted people to understand this before getting caught up in the trap. The sad fact is that we often don't realise what's happening until it's too late. Education on this issue is imperative.

ALCOHOL-INDUCED ANXIETY

Feelings of anxiety stemming from alcohol consumption can last for several hours up to an entire day after drinking. So, it follows that people who use alcohol as a coping mechanism for stress quickly fall into that pattern of alcohol dependency that only worsens the symptoms of anxiety. The immediate relief they feel is the reward that keeps them going back for more as there seems to be no other answer. The downward spiral into AUD becomes fact rather than fear. Those most vulnerable to falling into this trap are those who struggle with depression. When problems already seem impossible, the mindset is low, and it's often much more comfortable to accept a quick fix, anything for instant relief from the struggle within.

Matty realised this within his life and was desperate to help others avoid this painful pitfall.

DECISIONS

You see, this is the issue. A person struggling with depression can have an alcoholic drink or a drug to help them cope, and the brain becomes triggered into feeling better for a while. Feeling something good after being in a dark place is addictive.

Without education about the end result of this behaviour, the sufferer believes it's helping them get through their day. To feel that lift, to feel anything, is enticing. They think it's harmless, or worse, believe it's helping them because they are not in a good state of mind for decision making.

Matty fell into this trap, and the results wrecked his life for many years. He wanted people in this situation to know that while there is a quick lift, the addiction very quickly becomes so severe that you are experiencing all the symptoms you were trying to mask, while craving for the substance of choice. So, in a short space of time, the first problem has doubled!

He often told me he didn't know if it was the original anxiety or the need for a drink that caused his unwanted symptoms. It was indeed a never-ending cycle which caused him much anguish.

In the beginning, I was unaware Matty was using alcohol as a crutch. From my perspective, I thought he was doing so much better! He seemed happier and more settled. Naturally, this makes us feel relieved because our loved ones are more comfortable with life, or so we think. The perception is false and of course adds to the vicious cycle.

BRAIN CHEMICALS

To understand what is happening within our bodies, we need to know what our naturally occurring brain chemicals do for us.

I don't intend to get heavy in this book because I want the message to be quick and easy to put into practice while looking for solutions to issues that could be overwhelming you. While trying to find answers, there is so much confusing information. So, to put it quite simply, our bodies were designed to function at full potential and to heal when the need arises. They work like well-oiled machines. We have naturally occurring neurochemicals within our brain which work to our advantage:[32]

- Norepinephrine: acts as both a stress hormone and a neurotransmitter. It increases alertness and arousal and speeds up reaction time.

- Dopamine: a messenger involved in reward, motivation, memory, and regulating movement.

- Endorphins: At least 20 types interact with brain receptors to reduce your perception of pain. They trigger a positive feeling in the body similar to morphine, particularly after exercise.

- Anandamide: a fatty acid neurotransmitter associated with bliss and joy

- Serotonin: the key hormone that stabilises our mood, feelings of well-being and happiness. This hormone impacts our entire body and also helps with sleep and digestion, which is why it's often prescribed for depression.

These chemicals are enhanced in our brain when we are in a state of flow, more commonly known as being engrossed in something we love or energised focus. We gain a very natural lift when positively using our minds.

These are the chemicals I touched on earlier that have the ability to deplete as does our mood. Brain scans have shown that when we do something creative or uplifting, these neurochemicals increase. It naturally follows that when struck with a series of issues or a terrible loss, our mood lowers as do the brain-stimulating chemicals. A depressed mood is a result.

TIREDNESS OR DEPRESSION?

Depression also causes tiredness and lack of interest in doing things that used to be fun for the person struggling. Noticing if there is a lack of interest is an excellent way to tell the difference between plain tiredness and depression. When we are tired, we still feel motivated to do things we love but might say we're too tired and regret not being able to participate in our favourite activities. Depression, on the other hand, produces a feeling of no motivation. We are too tired to do things that used to be fun, but we also don't want to do them anyway. Another useful marker is if the person suffering still feels unmotivated and tired after a good night's sleep. The fatigue suffered due to depression permeates every facet of a person's life. Some examples are listed here:[33]

- Physically: Low mood, brain fog, tiredness, soreness or heaviness make the sufferer feel stiff and slow with aches and pains. Even getting dressed in the morning can be a challenge.

- Emotionally: Feelings of hopelessness, confusion, loss of self and loneliness make it challenging to interact with friends and family. It's easier to retreat than have to try harder than we are capable of at that moment.

- Cognitively: The brain fog and fatigue make it hard to stay focused, to process information and concentrate. Staying on task becomes almost impossible.

The symptoms are alarming, severe, and real. It's easy to understand why sufferers reach for something to dull their pain when they face conflicting ideas on why they feel this way.

A REWIRED BRAIN

Our brain is complex and surprising. It can form and reorganise synaptic connections, especially when learning something new or following an injury. Neuroplasticity is the name of this response. That's great news for stroke survivors but bad news for anyone dealing with addiction. In short, our brain becomes rewired by repeated exposure to anything. The brain scans of people suffering addiction clearly show this.[34] The sooner help is found the easier it will be to heal the brain.

DRUGS HARM THE BRAIN

Because of the way addiction rewires our brains, we can see that it is very harmful to try to mask depression or anxiety with drugs or alcohol. Our body has every chemical we need to function, but drugs give us only one at a time and in doing so create an imbalance in our bodies.

For example, people addicted to meth prefer this drug because it gives them a better attention span and more control. The naturally occurring norepinephrine typically does this job. They take cocaine to get the same high dopamine usually offers us. Heroin gives an artificial hit of endorphins. Antidepressants lift our serotonin levels to help us stay on task despite the pain. Herein lies the problem. Our brain, when balanced and happy, gives us all five *highs* right when we need them. No single drug will provide us with all five chemical highs. They each only give us one. So, when our brain receives an unnaturally high boost of one type of chemical, it adjusts to try to balance what we need. If we continually add more of that one chemical, the brain rewires, makes new pathways, altering our brain chemistry. The brain often sends confusing signals to the body when we use these drugs. I've heard of people who suffer a substance use disorder, needing artificial drugs to lift them up, then another type to bring them down again. It's staggering how we unsuccessfully try to take over the natural function of the brain. Sure, it works short term, but it can't be sustained indefinitely.

A person struggling with addiction will start having more symptoms and will need to take another drug to stop the negative feelings they have, thereby producing a deeper downward spiral. The brain patterns mess up and send signals of what it thinks it needs to recover, to which the person often responds by taking another type of pill.

Personally, I don't believe in any long-term drug-taking, if it's being used to mask depression; for example, how do we know what chemical is lacking in our brains? We might be low in dopamine, for example, but the doctor prescribes serotonin in a hope of lifting our depressed mood. Straight away, we have unbalanced the brain even further. Once on the path of dulling our problems/pain with alcohol or drugs, it is *a slippery slide downwards.* Matthew desperately wanted to get this exact message out there. Don't get caught up in substance misuse, because in the end, you will be far worse off than when you started. The good news is, the brain can be rewired again, but it takes time and commitment.

HOPE IS ETERNAL

There *is hope*, and there is a way out. We should not suppress the habits or shame the sufferer. I know many believe it's *the fault of the sufferer* because they *chose* to take the drugs or alcohol in the first place. Sure, they did, but how many of us reach for a painkiller when we're in pain? The problem is so much deeper than who took what or when. Healthy conversations to seek solutions is a great place to begin. Remember, they did not *choose* to develop depression or anxiety any more than someone else chose to have cancer. They need support, love, and care to get through, and they *can* heal if the desire and support is there.

Focus on your strengths, not your weaknesses.
Focus on your character, not your reputation.
Focus on your blessings, not your misfortunes.

—Roy T. Bennet

Part 2
CHANGING PERSPECTIVES

• • • | • • •

Renew Your Story

It's Never Too Late

THE SEARCH

MATTHEW STRUGGLED WITH depression, anxiety, and addiction for many years. His heart was huge, and his feelings deep. He continually searched for answers and opportunities to help others. He was a believer and often wrote the words *Hope Is Eternal* at the end of his writings.

There is nothing in this life which can prepare a mother for the loss of her child. Nothing. When faced with this reality, it doesn't feel real at all. But there are hopes, deep seated beliefs that help us continue on our path, sure in the knowledge of a future free of suffering.

A few days after my devastating loss, I was sitting in church, blinded by the tears that were to be my constant companion for many months to come. It was a comfortably warm day, and despite the tears, I felt comforted just being there, able to worship God. Through the window, I gazed across the green grass to see the branches of the trees gently swaying in the breeze. The sun's warmth permeated through the glass. I was in a world of my own, alone with God, when a well-meaning friend came and said that it was such a shame that I'd never see Matty again. Her words registered somewhere deep within. A seed was planted, but I simply replied, "Of course I'll see him again."

God's presence surrounded me. There was no room for doubt, and my faith was strong.

HIDDEN FEAR

That night, however, at around 2:00 a.m., I sat bolt upright in bed. Woken from my restless sleep by what, I wasn't sure. The words *You'll never see him again, never see him again, never see him again* repeatedly shattered my thoughts. I shuddered as I reached for my jacket. Slipping quietly out of bed, I walked into the living room, where on the floor, I saw so many boxes. Matty's whole life lived within them. All his writings, his poems, cards, and photos. Everything that meant something to him was right here. It had come down to this. Unbelievable. My mind was continually seeking God's; I felt His arms around me as I walked amidst the boxes. I reached down, my hand feeling a loose sheet of paper. I lifted it out and saw Matty's hand-writing. Pulling my jacket tightly around my shoulders, I sat down to read. It was a poem written by Matty many years before. With a broken heart and tear-filled eyes, I read these words:

AFTERLIFE

If life was a dream, would death mean life?
Will this nightmare end and happiness finally
will Heaven send?

Though a strange thought to harbour inside,
it's a mystery that each one must decide.

76

The answer is neither near nor far;
It's the strangest things that seem oddly bizarre.
It awakens the spirit; it's who we are.

Between me and you, hear this, my point of view,
Maybe that's why the world is blue,
For maybe this life will turn into two.

And this life is to learn about pain and greed,
Which stalks my heart to plant a seed
Now growing like a weed in a pot,
Dream with me, friend, as I say,
this ain't all we've got.

This time of pain will strengthen my soul
To accept the beauty I'll see when
My eyes open forever on that day of peace.

That day will surely come,
For it's sure to set as does the sun.

Closing my eyes, I'll draw my last breath,
For this moment, I'll suffer my first death.

Will I roll over and gasp for breath,
And open my eyes eternally free?

I wonder deep down if you'll be in front of me, smiling forever.

Imagine living only the good times,
Together in a perfect world which knows no pain or despair,
Eternal life with you I'd share.

—Matty Gibbs '06

RESSURECTION

It was Matty's belief put into words, his statement of faith. His surety from the grave.

I shuddered convulsively, crying to God with every bit of emotion I possessed. The first of many miracles with which God answered my fear. I knew I would see and hold my boy again, but the seed another person sowed in the deepest recesses of my mind had somehow sprouted into fear. I wasn't aware I was afraid, but God could see, and He sent me comfort. With every fibre of my being, I believe in the Resurrection; Matty did too. As I read Matty's writing, it felt like Matty spoke directly to me.

"Yes, Matty, I promise I will see you then. I will pray for you always and hold on with everything that is in me," I whispered.

PREMONITION

The thing that truly amazed me was that Matty's words contained the exact way he had passed from this world. "Closing my eyes, I'll draw my last breath, for this moment, I'll suffer my first death."

Matty had fallen asleep and not woken the next morning. There he was, looking very peaceful for all the world like he was sleeping. There had been no apparent reason for his passing. And I believed God had taken him. It would be months before we learned the exact cause and the details of the illness which eventually claimed his life.

COMPASSION

We must always assume the best in others. No one wants to live a depressed, unfulfilled life. The mistake of trying to cope by using alcohol or drugs does not make the sufferer a bad person. God alone knows their heart, and we need to show only love, not judgement.

I thank God for the example set by His dear Son. There are so many Bible stories which come to mind, where Jesus showed love and compassion for those whom others judged harshly.

Faith is the key because God may not answer the minute we ask. He may not even answer in this lifetime, not the way we might want anyway. Everything will happen in God's time, not ours.

Matty believed this but still felt the judgement of others very deeply and often told me he hated what his life had become but that it was not by choice. Matty felt as though he'd fallen into a deep, dark hole. There was a light in the distance, but he couldn't climb to it. He felt trapped. In his poem "Afterlife," he wrote about life being *blue*. "Maybe that's why this world is blue because this life will turn into two." Blue was Matty's term for sadness, but he never gave up hope. He often said, "Hope is eternal." He believed that if things didn't go right in this life, they would certainly work out in the next. He hoped that eventually, his life would work out and was planning for the best, but we don't know the reasons for anything. We must never give up!

Human nature limits our ability to believe or understand the unlimited power of God, but I am convinced our minds will be open to understanding when Jesus returns to the earth.

Faith in action is powerful, and God's love knows no bounds.

MASKING THE ISSUES

Once those who suffer with depression and anxiety begin to mask the signs by taking something to help them cope, life dives downwards. I feel this is where *stigma* begins. Others start to see the results instead of the person, in turn causing further pain for the one struggling to find an answer. I know it's hard, but we must look past this and seek solutions. The very life of your loved one depends on it. In the beginning, you might notice a glassy-eyed look or slightly slurred speech. Your gut tells you they have taken something. What is your reaction?

I understand that it's quite possibly annoyance or embarrassment. I felt this way many times. If these feelings are not put into check very quickly, the downward spiral will be more profound. Oh, Matthew taught me so much! I look back and see that he was, by far, the more insightful person. I had so much yet to learn. He taught me that my reaction of embarrassment or annoyance only led to a deeper attempt to mask, so the cycle continued. Fortunately, Matty was aware of this, and spoke openly about it, which helped me to understand on a much deeper level.

Everywhere we went, Matty would talk to people he thought were in need. He would tell complete strangers about his struggles if he thought it would help them. At that stage, I would feel mortified. I'd tell him not to make himself look bad to people who didn't even know us because what would they think? Oh my goodness, I'm ashamed of the way I thought in those days. My thoughts soften so much when I think of Matty's response. He would always put his arm around me and say, "Mumma, you just don't understand." He was so loving and not at all telling me off, even though I now think I should have been told off.

At his funeral, there were so many stories of how he helped people because they knew he would understand they could open up to him, and he always had the answers they needed. The whole reason he told his story was so others who struggled wouldn't feel alone.

There is a stigma about depression and anxiety that causes those who struggle to hide the fact that they are not feeling well. What we don't realise is that hiding the symptoms in this early stage actually causes a decline. It takes hard work to hide, and it's exhausting, so the person struggling often withdraws from loved ones so they can let down their guard. Having to cope on their own then makes them vulnerable to substance misuse. It's a very sad circle of decline, and we need to be aware of how our reactions will impact them. It's not easy, and we all make mistakes, but it's what we learn and how we move forward that counts.

HEIGHTENED AWARENESS

We might think we are masking our disapproval well, but your loved one who struggles has heightened awareness: they are acutely aware of their predicament and the reactions of those around them. If those reactions cause them to feel unworthy, think they have caused disappointment, didn't live up to expectations, or failed in some way, they will retreat, which is the last thing we want. Anxiety sets in, and the need to do something is acute.

When Matty used alcohol to get through the day, he would hide it, but he'd feel mortified if anyone ever noticed. I remember one such occasion where we had a wonderful family gathering. After everyone left, Matty came and told me he had a small amount from a whiskey bottle in the house. I reacted with anger, and he became distraught. He begged me not to tell anyone and that he would replace it. It was just a small amount, but I pushed the fact that it amounted to stealing no matter how little. This incident was one of the three times I remember Matty being overcome and overwhelmed. He was always honest with me, so he told me, and I cannot understand why I pushed it so hard on that day. Matty was beside himself at having done this and left distraught.

It saddened me to know it took Matty months to get over it when things like this happened. He desperately wanted to be like everyone else and hated that he had these problems.

He once told me people only seemed to remember the wrong things, which were so few compared to all the good things he did, but he felt judged on those few things, making it hard to cope. I regret these moments but am also thankful things were manageable most of the time, and Matty never gave up trying.

Today, when I hear stories from other families, I realise that what Matty did was so mild compared to what could have happened, but in some ways, I think my reaction to the small things kept him accountable to himself. He loved his family so much and hated to feel like a disappointment.

It frustrated me that he couldn't live his life the way he wanted. Every mother wants their child to be happy and healthy, and it's so painful to watch them decline, just like it must be if they suffer any other type of illness or injury that impacts their life so negatively.

During my life with Matty, I learned that the answer was to help him stay accountable while showing love and support. If our loved ones are trying to recover and haven't given up, then neither should we.

···2···
Define What's Needed

There Is No "One Size Fits All"

UNIQUE PERSONALITIES

SOME YEARS AGO, Matty and I were in town shopping, when Matty said, "I'll be back in a minute, Mumma." Dressed in shorts, a t-shirt, and thongs on his feet, he ran off towards a man sitting on the ground, leaning against the wall of a shop. I shook my head, as Matty was always doing this kind of thing.

I continued into the store to complete some shopping. Sometime later, Matty appeared beside me in bare feet. I looked down in amazement and asked where his shoes were. He said he had given them to the homeless man he had gone to speak with. At the time, I couldn't believe Matty was in the store with bare feet and on purpose.

Matty said, "Oh, Mumma, it made his day. No, I take that back. It made his week because he had nothing!"

I said, "Matty, you've got nothing." He put his arm around my shoulder and lovingly said, "But he really had nothing, far less than me."

There were so many of those moments throughout the years with Matty. I thought he was so different from anyone else I knew. Material possessions meant nothing to him. Money was just a means to an end, and he always shared everything he had. I look back and ponder that day often. Matty was extremely agitated, full of anxiety, yet he still could not pass a person in need.

My eyes fill with tears every time I think of how he suffered and how much I lacked understanding of him. You see, each person is unique. No two of us are precisely the same. We all have different needs and our own ideas on what is right and wrong. When trying to support a loved one or friend who is struggling with anxiety or depression, we need to put ourselves in their shoes. That's not easy, I know. We, too, are a product of our upbringing and have our own set of problems, but this is life. I understand how a carer's life is changed by having someone in the home who struggles in such a way. It's no different than caring for someone with cancer or a broken leg, for example. It takes compassion and commitment. It is truly exhausting, but ask yourself, "What choice do I have?" I didn't care to think of the alternative, so as hard as it was, I pushed through each day while trying my best to support him. With the benefit of hindsight, it was the right thing to do without a shadow of a doubt.

EFFECTS OF DEPRESSION

You will need to look at the unique personality type of your loved one to work out how depression will affect them. I know I've written it before, but it's so important not to try to slot your loved one into what someone else tells you is right, especially if that someone doesn't have to suffer the consequences of it all going wrong.

I think it's a lot like bringing up little kids. Some only need a stern look to keep them out of harm's way, while others will run you ragged trying to keep them healthy and safe. No two are the same. That doesn't change as they get older.

Matty was always so full of love and so funny; he made us all laugh so often. He could imitate any character and was so fond of comedians like Jim Carrey. He would repeat whole scenes from comic movies in the actors' voices. Oh, how we laughed. He would also imitate people who were out fishing, from YouTube videos. Matty possessed a marvellous mind, yet he felt he didn't fit into this world, even from a young age.

He was often in trouble at school because his character rubbed the teachers the wrong way. I didn't know this until long after he had left school. He told me many stories where he felt bullied, and I felt so bad for him and worse because he hadn't asked for help while it was going on!

I realise now this was an integral part of his character. He did not like anyone to suffer from feeling bad, so he kept all his problems to himself, even as a child! As I write this, light bulbs are going off in my head. Oh my goodness, I feel like the worst parent ever.

One time when I was cooking, his little head popped around the corner. Matty would have been about ten. Only his face showed which looked so cute, so I grinned at him until I noticed he didn't look right. He said, "Mummy, I've got something to tell you, but please don't be upset."

I instantly panicked!

As I write this, it has been five years since Matty passed, and I haven't been able to go through his albums. I remember I made him a beautiful photo album of his life to that point for his eighteenth birthday. Added in little pockets were personal letters to him as a keepsake for long after I was gone. That was the plan anyway.

I've just pulled out that album and turned to the page of this day. In the little pocket was a letter I wrote to him. It reads:

Dearest Matty,

I'll never forget the day you broke your arm! Your consideration of my feelings really touched my heart.

I was in the kitchen cooking when your little head popped around the corner. You said, "Mummy, I've got something to tell you, but please don't be upset." You knew me so well. I began to panic and asked you what the matter was—I could tell by your face that something was very wrong. You said, "Please don't worry, but I think I've broken my arm." Still, only your little head was showing. I rushed toward you, feeling sick inside. You thought you broke your arm, you poor little man. Your forearm was hanging down in the centre like a letter "U." Your arm was broken alright. Through all that pain, your first consideration was not to frighten me even though you were so young. I appreciate your love for me, and I am so proud of your courage and strength.

I'll love you forever,
Mum xxxxxxxxx

He was more concerned for me because he knew I would worry for him. It's these characteristics that don't change in a person. As an adult, Matty would still put others before himself and could never bear to see others suffer. This is why he felt he had to help every homeless person he saw or anyone who suffered depression or anxiety and try to stop them from going into the downward spiral. It was so important to him and now so important to me to send his message out to the world.

NUTRITION

Nutrition plays a vital role in healing. We all know that by design, our bodies will heal, but correct nutrients are needed. Herein lies another potential problem, as there are two kinds of people:

- Those who are comfort eaters
- Those who cannot eat when under stress

It seems there is no middle ground when we are stressed out. There is a problem with both scenarios, but from experience, I'd say it is better to have a low appetite. I used to make green smoothies for Matty when he couldn't eat due to anxiety. That way, he didn't have to force himself to eat because it was easy to sip a smoothy, and it was full of nutrients. A favourite was green apples, celery, cucumber, silver beet, and a whole lemon. YUM.

Previously, I was one who would not eat when under stress, but this past year, I have become a comfort eater! That is much harder to control. The biggest problem with comfort eating is that we rarely reach for a carrot stick! It's usually anything we can get our hands on because our cravings control our behaviour unless we are persistently mindful. Again, if depression or anxiety is current, mindfulness usually isn't.

THE BRAIN AND GUT CONNECTION

Since I introduced the connection between the brain and the gut earlier, I've investigated this topic at length, and the conclusion seems to be that there is a direct link between diet and mental health. Of course, it's not so simple that we can eat our way to happiness, but a good, clean diet combined with exercise seems to be the answer.

People have also reported a much clearer mind after fasting. Perhaps because with a healthier gut, the messages to the brain transmit with greater ease. A healthy mind comes from an overall approach to good health within our body.

Studies on this connection provide valuable information for those struggling with depression. (I will only give a brief overview here, but if this interests you, I'd highly recommend a more in-depth study on the matter.)

Within the walls of your digestion system is found "the brain in your gut," known as the enteric nervous system (ENS). It is comprised of over 100 million nerve cells. These cells line the tract from the oesophagus, all the way down to the rectum. This system is responsible for controlling digestion by releasing the enzymes to break down the food, allow nutrient absorption, and eliminate waste. Quite incredible!

From the time of our birth, and continuing throughout life, we acquire a broad diversity of microbiota in our gut. There is approximately one kilo of bacteria working within by the time we reach adulthood. Eye-opening stuff! Although not conclusive, studies reveal that a broader range of microbes gives us better protection from depressive issues. Exercise promotes a greater diversity in the microbiota, something I found particularly interesting.

If harmful bacteria get a chance to flourish within our gut, it causes inflammation which interrupts the passage of the compounds needed to regulate our mood. Use of antibiotics is one reason this could happen.

Studies into particular diets have shown the Mediterranean diet, including fermented food in conjunction with exercise, as having significant benefits for mood disorders by positively impacting mental health. This type of diet contains the nutrients needed for the gut, and there is no need for probiotic supplements when on this diet.

In previous years, doctors believed depression could cause stomach upsets, such as diarrhoea, constipation, or irritable bowel syndrome (IBS). Researchers now believe it's most likely the other way around. When we do not have good gut health, these conditions send signals to the central nervous system, triggering mood changes and conditions such as anxiety and depression. Another extremely interesting fact is that although serotonin is well known as one of the valuable brain neurotransmitters, over ninety percent of the serotonin in our body is made in the digestive track. It's known as peripheral serotonin and is stored in platelets. The level of serotonin in the blood is determined by its production in the gut. Low levels of serotonin have been linked to diseases such as IBS, cardiovascular disease, and osteoporosis. Doctors are now treating IBS with commonly known anti-depressants containing serotonin.[35]

WHAT DOES THIS MEAN FOR US?

We gain a better understanding of the links between our digestive health and our moods through this type of research. A better understanding of gut issues provides us with new opportunities to heal.

The bottom line is that we need to eat a healthy, balanced diet while paying particular attention to the needs of the gut. Without the correct balance, the nerves in the stomach lining cannot send the right signals for digestion. Other responses kick in, and our mood lowers, which is a good reason to eat healthy and keep an eye out for further research on this topic.

FOOD FOR THOUGHT

It's crucial to have various foods in your diet—different coloured vegetables to ensure a balance because each provides unique nutrients. I like to keep things simple, so when making smoothies, I would swap the types of greens every couple of days, but that was as far as I went. I always made them in the thermomix, full of fibre, but they can be done in a standard juicer too. I include a few combinations we loved that are easy to throw into the thermie and are so nutritious. You can experiment with any combinations and amounts.

Green Smoothie
Kale or baby spinach leaves
Green apple
Lime juice
Cucumber
Avocado
Coconut water
Ice cubes

Carrot Crush
Carrots
Celery
Green apple
Whole lemon
Coconut water
Ice cubes

Ginger Ninja
Carrots
Red apple
1-inch piece of fresh ginger
Celery
Coconut water
Ice cubes

To get extra vegetables into the diet, I like to make a white sauce with cauliflower instead of plain flour. I always have a batch of this in the freezer. I use it as the base for tuna mornay or any dish which requires a white sauce. It can also be used just as a sauce to go with corned silverside.

Cauliflower Sauce
1/2-head of cauliflower
1 cup of milk
2 egg yolks
1/2-cup grated cheese (to taste)
Salt and pepper

Method:
Cut the cauli into bite-sized pieces and place in the thermomix with the milk.

Cook on 100, speed 1 for 20 minutes or until cauli is cooked.

Drain milk and save.

Add cheese, egg yolks, and seasoning.

Blitz for 60 seconds, speed 10 until smooth, adding a small amount of the saved milk to achieve a dollop cream consistency if needed.

That's it; easy to make, freezes well, and can also be made on the stovetop if you don't have a thermomix.

THE HEART OF THE MATTER

In researching the brain-gut connection, I came across a third connection. I touched on this earlier in the book, so I wanted to give a bit more information here. I always intended for this book to be an easy read and didn't want to get bogged down in pages of scientific data, but there is enough information out there to warrant comments on this third connection, which is the heart.

Now, as I researched this, I realised it's only natural and right that there should be such connections within our bodies. After all, by design and given the right environment, we live, breathe, and heal. No system runs alone.

We already know of the connection between the mind and the gut, but we see that a heart-mind interaction also takes place. Electrical signals travel along the spinal cord nerves via the vagus, which is the nerve primarily responsible for many crucial bodily functions, including heart rate, digestion, immune response, and mood control. The heart is also an endocrine gland, so chemicals are also involved in the interactions with the brain.

Recent studies show through the vagus nerve, the heart sends signals to the brain that are not only understood but are also acted upon. At first, this information blew my mind. For example, if you are running, the heart sends messages to the brain about how hard it is pumping and sends further commands to control how quickly it beats. Still, scientists have discovered neural pathways whereby input from the heart facilitates or inhibits the brains electrical activity, allowing both the gut and the heart-mind to work together to help in the overall thought process and in creating a feeling of well-being.

You will have heard expressions such as *trust your gut* or *go with your heart*. We have always likened emotional pain or decisions as being heartfelt, while matters of intuition as being felt in the gut. Research shows that these are not only metaphors but that in actuality, there may be scientific explanations for this thought process. Recent studies show your heart receives intuitive information before the brain. Quite possibly, this explains why we stress over *doing* certain things that don't *feel* right. I know this answers a lot of indecision I have within my own life. It feels good to know!

The more I study this concept, the more I feel we need to develop a greater trust for our *instincts.*

• • •3• • •
Time for Change

Practical Solutions

Insanity is doing the same thing over and over again, but expecting different results.

—*Rita Mae Brown*

WELL, IT'S NOT exactly insanity, but you get the message of this quote. We are all guilty of doing the same things over and over while wondering why we can't achieve the outcome we want. We tend to get stuck in what's familiar, and sometimes it's hard to make a change. When someone has depression or anxiety, it's even more challenging, but we must make a change!

In this chapter, I'm going to delve into seven specific changes we can easily make. It's often easier to stay as we are, but that won't facilitate the change we need to heal. Those struggling with prolonged depression will quite likely not be in the headspace for change. They will resist and come up with every negative reason why it won't work. With support, belief, and help from loved ones or friends, relatively quickly, you'll see the difference, and they will feel so much better.

Once they reach this mindset, it's a lot easier for them to manage their condition, knowing they have support.

WHY OUR PERCEPTION MATTERS

Some years ago, researchers from Cornell and the University of California used Facebook to conduct an experiment in which they intentionally played with the emotions of 689,003 users by manipulating their news feeds. Some users merely saw negative stories, while others only saw positive stories. Sure enough, when these people later posted updates, they were greatly influenced by the mood of the posts they'd previously viewed in their feed. None of the "participants" gave their consent to join the study, so naturally, people were upset once the experiment was made public. More frightening than this was realising how easily emotions could be altered by subtle manipulation.[36]

RAS FILTER

But what about the stories we tell ourselves? We are greatly influenced by what we see and what we allow into our conscious mind, even from our ourselves. When someone is in a low or depressed state, they cannot see the good that is right in front of them. The reason they sink lower and lower is that, without realising it, they are sabotaging themselves. That is the way our mind works.

We have a filter in the brain which screens out most of our subconscious thoughts and only lets what we need or ask into our conscious vision. Without this filter, we would be entirely overwhelmed by the incoming mass of stimulation. It's known as the reticular activating system, or RAS filter. Our subconscious mind takes in four billion bits of information every second, but our conscious brain only processes around 40 to 200 bits of this. An easy way to explain how this works is if I ask you to look around and find something blue. Your RAS filter will immediately jump into gear and start bringing up the colour blue from everything around you. The colour was always there, but you didn't notice it. Your focus is now on blue, and you will quickly see blue everywhere. So, our mind will search for and make real what we are telling or asking it.[37]

That is also the reason there is such power in positive thoughts, but sadly, that is not the thought process of a person struggling with depression. They often tell themselves negative things, so their RAS filter is continuously on the lookout for negativity and, suddenly, BOOM! It appears to be true! The downward spiral takes hold. There can, however, be an upside to this.

Remember the story of Abraham Lincoln in part one? I believe he was able to perceive a crisis so quickly because he was focused on negativity. His RAS filter actually looked for bad things to happen due to his depression. Quite incredible. Of course, no one wants to be unhappy all the time, so there is a certain amount of sadness in his accomplishments.

SUPPORT AND MINDSET

You might be able to see why a person who feels depressed needs support and guidance to change their mindset. They need love and someone who believes in them.

Continual input of positivity goes a long way in bringing their thoughts to a higher level. When you try to encourage them and they say they can't, they mean it. It's impossible to see the good when our mind is in this state, and you can't just snap your fingers to change the mindset. It then follows that people who say a depressed person has to pull themselves together and do it on their own need to know it will never happen. This is a sad attitude, and we've all been there, but worse, we say it to those we love. Support is urgently needed to enable a change. Once the positivity and belief around them start to sink in, then they have a much better chance of lifting their thought process, and the words "I can" are used more often.

Again, this highlights that our long-held beliefs are wrong. If our loved one told us they had cancer, would we say, "Well, I can't support you with this. You need to pull yourself together to feel better?" Of course not, so why are we like this when our loved one is struggling with their mental health? Please make no mistake; they are suffering, and it's not a choice. We can make a huge difference, so, as promised, here are the seven changes we can easily make to improve life for those struggling with depression or anxiety:

1—A GOOD SENSE OF SELF

Building a great sense of self is paramount in developing a new mindset. You will notice those struggling with depression will often sound very negative. Sufferers are often particularly down on themselves, and that needs to change. The significant loss I wrote about earlier is more often than not a loss of self. The further down that path they go, the harder it is to climb out. Strategies need to be put in place to build self-esteem. If our loved ones only see the negativity around them, we need to encourage them and keep them close as friend or family. If we have a judgemental attitude toward them, they will withdraw, and this is when the downward spiral is most likely to take hold. To encourage, support, love, and tell them you believe they can do it is the first, but essential, step toward healing.

2—CREATIVITY HEALS

There is an incredible range in what is known as *being creative* today. Anything you make that did not exist previously

96

in precisely the same form is something created! So, there's no excuse not to get into it. Modern psychologists believe being creative in any way supports good mental health. Anything enjoyable should be encouraged. From gardening to crossword puzzles, writing, or drawing, it's all beneficial to well-being and good mental health.

Matty would write and draw often. He wrote in rhyme; it just seemed to come out that way. One of the rhyming stories I found after he passed was four chapters long and was the story of his life during a particularly turbulent time. I thought it unique! He would draw, doodle, or write on anything available, even paper napkins. He was gifted and incredibly creative, and I'm sure this helped him get through many a rough patch.

3—SELF-CARE

Putting yourself first is not something that comes easily to people who are *givers*. That's because we often have a warped view of what self-care is. It doesn't mean to take the first and best of everything while trampling over others—not at all.

It means to take care of yourself, to be the best you can be in mind and body so you have plenty of energy left over to support others. That's it! We all know the expression *you can't pour from an empty cup,* don't we? So, fill yourself up to overflowing! Expressing yourself is a necessary form of self-care too.

4—MUSIC

Now, this is always a touchy subject for those struggling with depression, especially teens. We all have different tastes in music, but music has power, and we need it to have a positive effect on our mindset.

One of my kids' teachers told me once my child's choice of music was detrimental to his mental health. At the time,

I thought he was overdramatic, and I disagreed with him. Thankfully, nothing wrong came of that story, but when I look back, I now understand what he meant.

Think about this scenario: If someone you love is in a depressed state of mind and they are playing music to match their mood, what do you think will happen? They will stay stuck in their depressed mood. It's such a simple concept yet one we don't think on often. A definite choice is needed to lift the sufferer out of the low state. It's an act of faith. We don't know the outcome, but we make a better choice, believing a change for the better will be the outcome. A different option in music has the power to lift us, and that is the desired effect needed when in a depressed state of mind.

I experienced this recently, and the outcome was a powerful message. It was on the anniversary of Matty's passing last October. I thought I was okay but decided to stay away from social media so nothing would trigger me. You see, our bodies have a memory and will often reignite that trauma on the anniversary of or leading up to the painful day. These traumatic feelings can revisit us for years without us even realising it. Every year as it neared the month in which Matty passed, I would become emotional and suffer many unwanted symptoms. I would end up crying for days over the simplest little memory and didn't understand it until a doctor told me about our body's ability to remember these events, even if we try to block it from our mind.

On this particular month, last year, I was feeling okay and thought, *Finally, I can survive the day without breaking!* How wrong I was.

I ventured onto Facebook to do a favour for my sister, and the first post there was one of remembrance of Matty. It was like a dam bursting; my grief was instant. Losing a child is like sailing into unchartered waters. People tell us what grief is like, the stages of grief, and what to expect, but it is nothing like they say. True, some days are calm sailing. Most others, a memory will trigger emotions like sudden turbulence on the ocean. Worst of all, like an unexpected storm, grief erupts, almost drowning in its effect and rendering us incapable of anything else but hanging on and riding it through.

Even though I thought I was okay that day, the emotion was still there, just under the surface, lurking and waiting for its moment to escape. I cried and cried and shared my "Matty Memories" on Facebook, which often consoles me through my grief. There is a desperate feeling of not wanting him forgotten by anyone. As a mother, you don't want your child left behind ever.

A compassionate friend left me a song in the comments. He wrote, "Lifting you up in prayer right now; I can't imagine the pain. We both know the healer. This is the song I am sending you." I listened to that song all day— "It Is Well" by Kristene DiMarco I played it over and over and could feel my mood lifting. Of course, the prayer had a lot to do with it, too, because I felt so close to God. I realised what we listen to has a significant impact on our emotions, and it is so important not to listen to dark music or lyrics when in a low state of mind. Music truly has the power to heal, especially if there is a deeper meaning of faith behind the words.

We all need something on which to hold. Encouragement is so important when we feel low. Think about the type of music your loved one usually listens to when not in a depressed state. Pieces that have good memories attached are an excellent choice. Perhaps songs played in the car during holidays or outings. Each person's choice will be different, which is okay as long as it's uplifting music. If your loved one who suffers depression appears caught in a trap of spiralling lower because of their music choice, then perhaps play something different when in their company. Talk, listen, and be as positive as you can.

Everything helps in a small way.

5—MEDITATION/PRAYER AND SLEEP

There are three main aspects involved in good health. One involves the quiet times where we calm our mind and body through relaxing activities such as reading, meditating, and prayer, to name a few. The second follows on from this and involves getting enough sleep. The last is exercise, where we get our heart rate up to release neurochemicals that give us a lift and alleviate stress. All are needed equally. We can't always be on the run and expect our minds to be calm. A balance is needed for complete heath.

Meditation of some kind is essential for carers and sufferers alike. We are all trying to cope the best we can.

I think it's worth repeating that it is good to have hope and something grounding on which to hold. My faith, along with Bible reading and meditation, has carried me through so much in this life. I'm happy that Matthew had that deep belief which carried him onward during his short life too.

When coping with severe anxiety or depression, it's crucial to have many quiet times throughout the day. Overactive minds won't slow down by themselves. It is, however, tough to be still long enough to quiet the mind when it is racing. Bear this in mind when supporting your loved one through anxiety.

SLEEP STORIES

One of my favourite ways of relaxing the mind is with sleep stories. Until recent years, I had never heard of sleep stories for grown-ups, but it's a logical progression from the bedtimes stories we heard as kids. I love sleep stories, and there are many available for free online if you search. The other way is to buy an app to have them at your fingertips when needed. I don't know if it's just me, but I have never heard the end of one of these stories. They are just so relaxing; I drift off to sleep long before the end. The idea, of course, is to quiet the mind long enough for sleep to take hold.

During a particularly turbulent time in my life, I would fall asleep exhausted while listening to a sleep story, then awake within a couple of hours. I put the story on again, even if I had to do it a few times during the night. The idea is to stop your mind from overthinking, worrying about potential disasters that our logical mind knows are never really likely to happen. Repeatedly waking and replaying a story can be frustrating, but the alternative of being awake for most of the night with an overactive mind is unthinkable, not to mention unhealthy.

Good quality sleep is really important, so seek help if you or your loved one are not achieving this.

THE QUIET MIND

During the day, it's a good idea to stop and calm your mind at intervals so you don't become overwhelmed.

I want to add a word of caution regarding meditation. Sometimes we find it very hard to meditate and feel we are actually feeling worse or confused. If this is the case, don't push it. We often think meditation is always beneficial, so we have to push through. In fact, if you are dealing with complex issues, trauma, or a hyper body state, meditation should only be practised slowly and gently. Stop if you feel overwhelmed. It will only be for a short time until you are not in such a heightened state of anxiety.

When we are in a state of anxiousness, or having panic attacks, our body is in a state of high alert. Trying to meditate can confuse your brain. Firstly, the brain is coping with this hyper-vigilant state and looking for the perceived threat out there somewhere, but here you are trying to relax through meditation. Your brain interprets this as letting your guard down and can step up the need to be vigilant. It's a more common occurrence than we realise and can actually make your unwanted symptoms worse. It took me quite a while to work this out, but now I love meditation. It does get better and easier. The trick is to take time each day in meditation never to reach the unwanted hyper state.

Time spent meditating, even for short spans, is very beneficial. Time spent in prayer talking to our Heavenly Father is life-altering. Whatever it is you prefer to do is fine as long as it is something that slows your mind, especially if you are experiencing racing thoughts.

The danger in having a continually racing mind is that it can't be on high alert indefinitely. Something has to give; hence, the idea of calming the mind at regular intervals throughout the day and making sure you get an adequate amount of sleep.

I have an e-book called *The Quiet Mind* on my website. It's a beginners guide to meditation which I'd love to gift you.

Go to www.KarenGibbs.com.au to download your free copy.

6—EXERCISE

Exercise enhances our health in many ways and produces a feeling of wellbeing. It's said to improve the outcomes of chronic diseases such as heart disease and diabetes and aids in the lowering of blood pressure. It also alleviates many symptoms of mental-health issues, helps in weight control, and promotes a better quality of sleep—all excellent reasons to exercise daily.

Because we now understand there is a strong brain-gut connection, it is important to remember exercise promotes greater diversity of the microbiota in the gut. These microorganisms contribute to the transporting of healthy signals to the brain. They boost our overall health because they make up an ecosystem within our core that adapts to each of us individually. So, in effect, our gut becomes a mirror of us.

Medical facts aside, exercise makes us feel good, and that's a great reason to make time for physical activity each day.

We need to manage depression and anxiety as an overall health issue and not focus on only one aspect. A far better outcome and overall good health will be the result.

Exercise kicks off a biological series of events within our body resulting in a deep feeling of well-being. High-intensity exercise releases endorphins, which are the body's feel-good chemicals. It's this high that people who jog will tell you feels fantastic: a natural high. The real health benefits are in low-intensity exercise sustained over time. That kind of activity spurs the release of proteins which cause nerve cells to grow and make new connections which in turn improve brain function. Exercise also stimulates the area of the brain that regulates mood, so it's an all-round win.

THE STRUGGLE TO BEGIN EXERCISE

There are some notable reasons why people who struggle with depression feel they can't get out and exercise. It has nothing to do with laziness, although this is another label they often have to endure.[38]

1. Deficient Dopamine Levels
2. Leaden Paralysis
3. Social Anxiety
4. Self-Stigma
5. Negative Self-Talk

It is not helpful to tag a person as lazy because they say they cannot exercise. Encouragement and accompanying them for a short, easy walk, for example, will yield far better results.

It is clear to all that exercise is beneficial, but beginning exercise is the hard part. Those struggling with severe depression don't have motivation because of low dopamine, the neurotransmitter that makes you feel excited and enthusiastic. With decreased levels, a person will feel very tired and lacking in energy. We may feel they are "lazy," but this is not the case. The brain chemistry is saying not to get up and move—it's a self-preservation mechanism.

Sometimes people experience debilitating physical symptoms that stop them from exercising. One such symptom is heavy limbs that feel unable to move. This is one of the key symptoms of *atypical depression* and can vary from person to person. Other signs and symptoms may include:

- Depression that temporarily lifts in response to good news or positive events
- Increased appetite or weight gain
- Sleeping too much but still feeling sleepy in the daytime
- Sensitivity to rejection or criticism, which affects your relationships, social life or job

Atypical depression is usually chronic and often occurs if there is a blood relative who also has the disorder. This is one of those inherited traits I wrote about earlier in the book that perhaps Lincoln may have been suffering.

Once in the rut of feeling low and not exercising, food can often become a key focus. Many use food for comfort—I've been there myself. It's not a great combination to overeat while avoiding exercise, but many people, unfortunately, find themselves in this position. Weight gain happens, causing further anxiety and feelings of low self-esteem. It is an awful cycle, and many people will tell you the weight gain seemed to occur before they even realised it. Of course, weight doesn't just appear, but the thing is, the person was feeling so low they weren't paying attention. Back to why self-care is vital!

Once the person finds themselves in this position, self-stigma and low self-esteem become the norm. When people feel depressed, there is a constant tirade of negative self-talk in their heads, telling them they are failures. Instead of feeling optimistic about any exercise they do accomplish, they will think it isn't good enough, and feelings of hopelessness are likely to stop them from trying again.

It's so sad to see a loved one caught in this cycle, yet it is all too familiar. Lots of support and good health management will produce a successful outcome over time. Understanding the reasons why there is a problem is an excellent place to start. Changing habits at a slow pace will give better results; for example, if the sufferer goes for a short walk or bike ride first thing each morning and gradually builds it up, improvement will follow. It's breaking the old patterns for long enough to make a change and not doing it in a rush causing the individual to give up almost before they begin.

7—GRATITUDE JOURNALING AND OTHER WRITING

Writing is an excellent form of self-expression. Writing with gratitude in mind is very uplifting. Matty wrote often. Pouring his thoughts out by hand was healing for him. It's cleansing and therapeutic to write out our ideas and innermost thoughts.

Many therapists encourage clients to keep a gratitude journal. A depressed mind leads to depressed and often negative thoughts, so being intentional to write out our positive thoughts helps retrain the brain. Being thankful gives us a reason to look outside of ourselves and to use positive self-talk. It's very empowering for someone suffering depression to take an active role in their recovery. One small step leads to much bigger steps.

Matthew wrote whatever came to his mind and found it kept track of his fears and deepest thoughts when they often felt jumbled in his head. I liken it to filing away the information, putting it into an order to make sense of what's happening, but he also wrote for a better future.

••4•••

In Matty's Own Words

"Hope Is Eternal"
—Matthew Gibbs

MATTHEW OFTEN WROTE in rhyme. His words came naturally in a pattern. He wrote to empty his mind of his worries and thoughts, as well as to help others. I remember when the wildlife warrior, Steve Irwin, died in a tragic accident, Matty was devastated; we all were. Our farm in Landsborough bordered land owned by Australia Zoo, and we looked upon the Irwin family as neighbours even though we didn't know them personally. However, along with most of the world, we loved them all. Matty and his friends picked so many flowers and took them around to the zoo. We all felt personally grieved!

A couple days later, our little terrier caught and injured a snake, and we had to call the zoo for help. By the time the zoo staff arrived, the snake had died, but to our surprise, they had brought "Baby Bob," as we called him then, along.

He was so blonde, cute, and tiny, but he still wanted to see that snake. My heart almost broke as I thought of his family and what they now must endure. He was so like his dad, even at that stage of his young life. I didn't know that I, too, would be facing the greatest tragedy of my life in time to come. Life is like that: startling and often frightening in its intensity. Matty was gutted and took to writing as a coping mechanism. He wrote the words that I've included in this chapter on one of his sheets of art paper. He felt this loss so deeply.

Although not what he intended, Matty's writings show an excellent example of journaling towards empowerment by replacing the negatives with hope and positive words.

I'm on this mission because of Matthew and his writing, so I'm dedicating this chapter to it. I know his words will resonate with those who struggle with depression and the many resulting pitfalls. Matthew would love that his words were an encouragement for others. Some stories describe his deep pain, while others, his hope.

Matty's beautiful nature and deep-thinking mind was a blessing, although it caused him plenty of grief, as all sensitive souls will understand. Matty believed; he believed in hope and in never giving up. No matter how difficult things became, wherever he went, he encouraged others.

THE FIRST CUT

If I tried to look into your heart, what would I see?
And if I gazed into your eyes, would you see me?

If I touched you, would you feel me,
And if by chance I loved you, would you love me too?
If I made you a promise, would you see it through?
I wish I'd asked all these things of you.

I looked for answers deep down inside;
I ran I fell I begged, I cried.

In Matty's Own Words

I want you to know you took my pride.

You told me once that I was your one,
You made a promise from which you will forever run.

I guess you're only human and what's done is done.

I guess you forgot those things you said;
From the moment I met you, I was already dead.

Giving my heart to you made me feel whole,
But when you took it away like everything else,
Not only did you break me, but you crushed my soul.

I can't show you the damage you caused,
I wanted to hold you close, and I tried my best,
Lonely and weak now and always depressed.

Sometimes I cry when I remember your lies,
Your ways, your anger, your bitter goodbyes.

My hands go numb, and my whole body shakes
When I taunt myself with your selfish mistakes.

You betrayed everything I believed in and all that I knew.
In a moment, you forgot who you were and why our love grew;
You made a choice we could never undo.

A deep pain surrounds me when I think of what happened
that night;
Why did you forget us, was I that out of sight?

Nothing you could say would make this right;
What made you realise my greatest fear,
Or take so long to tell me, it was over a year?

I lost part of my soul each time I cried,
Was I dead or alive? I could never decide,
Plagued by the memories and visions of what we lost,
And how hard I fought, regardless the cost.

I lost the respect of my whole family for you;
I lost friends for life to keep what we grew.

I lost my life and mind, and all for you.

You gave me eyes; you made me see,
You showed me how low a human could be.

Through my suffering, I'm starting to see;
You never left me; you set me free.
I take comfort in who I am now.
I've regained my pride by knowing who I am.
I believe in real honesty, and forever,
I'm now a man, hope always, at least that's the plan!

MY ANGER

You're everything that's wrong with me . . .
Your selfish ego crushed my perfect soul,
Your bitter heart took everything beautiful and made it pain.
Your beautiful eyes stole my eyes and took my breath,
They broke my heart, now I long for death . . .

You wouldn't know love if it crushed your chest;
So go on you heartless devil as you take another soul,
Live your empty life as you follow your crazy heart.

Don't ever forget that life you stole—
Remember me, baby?

Yeah that's right your old boy,
Remember your so-called "one,"
The one you stole.

So go on, go on take another,
You wouldn't know love
If it crushed your chest,
So go on ...
Go on ...

DESTINY?

Years passed us by and fate struck your eye,
It started the end and it created a lie.
It took away hope, my ability to cope,
My soul is lost, my heart is torn;
Is our fate known before we are born?
Is life supposed to be this cold?

I once had you and I swore always to keep your heart warm
and close by,
To me a promise is until you die,
Now all I can do is watch as you break my heart,
Pain is within me and that's just the start.
I'm haunted by grief to the end of days,
I've lost hope and joy,
I miss your ways.

LOST ...

The sound of a thousand broken souls echo from the depth
of his very being.
He is at one with pain, and the very meaning of loss haunts
his life.

His blue eyes are truly blue and the light that once shone from them is now gone forever,
His smile has become a vision known only in his dreams, his blood runs cold now,
The warmth brought only by the one he loved is gone forever,
His fears are real and his pain deeper than the world itself.

With tears on his pillow, he remembers the one who forgot him,
The soul can lose itself but to lose a friend is unbearable,
She'll never know, she'll never care my tears are forever . . .

SOCIETIES PRISON

As I sit here alone in my mind, tears falling from an empty soul, I look back on my life and what it has become. Where do I even begin when it's all said and done? As my whole world caves in around me, I take a step back. I take in what's happening to my life and what I've turned into. Suddenly, in a moment, I realised that I don't even know who I am anymore. My depression is consuming me. Will happiness ever find me, or has it forgotten where to look? I want to feel free! Societies prison is using me up and playing me in every part of its game, or so it seems. I'm scared it will spit me out on the other side a sad old man. From these depths of despair that I can't escape, I can clearly see what I'm missing. I hate myself more every day for not standing up for myself and not giving my mind and body what it truly needs. I feel so lost, and I need a break somewhere. I think it's the only way to escape from depression and addiction. This life is killing me: maybe I'm better off dead. Perhaps that's what's meant to be, or so it seems right now, but really, life is what you make it!

MOVING ON

His heart is pure and his mind complete,
Though his shattered soul will forever bear the scars of his
broken past.

He has filled his empty life with hope.
His cup overflows now with the happiness he tried so desperately to find.

The compassion of his family and the love of his closest
friends have shown him new hope, and a new reason to live.

He gazes into the sky and sometimes thanks God for the
chance he thought he'd never see, though he knows that now
he must give, give all for this new life.

It's a new day, and from the depths of despair,
He's reached a place where the stars can dance in his eyes.
Hope is the foundation for happiness;
Without it, he's lost.
Look into his eyes—
Can you see his hope?

With life on his side . . . watch him fly!

BELIEVE

There is some hope for those who believe,
Though first you must give before you receive.

Give up your life, or the one you know,
It's time to live; it's time to grow.

Stop the Downward Spiral

Give up the things that are taking your health,
You know it's wrong, you're killing yourself.

Hold your weakened mind high and try not to cry,
As day by day, you say goodbye.

Goodbye to the things that have made you blue,
Goodbye to the sadness that one became two.

Goodbye to the stress of the life you knew.

Set a goal and stick to your word,
Live up to the promises that many have heard.

It won't come for free, but soon you will see,
Become the man; the best you can be!

Just hold on and ride through the pain,
Know in yourself what you stand to gain.

Hold onto hope and don't let that go.

Use all that you are and all that you know.

This is your chance you can't let it go.

Follow your heart and believe in your soul;
Believe in its ability to reach this goal.

Do all these things, and very soon, I'm sure,
That where there was less, now will be more.

You'll wake up one day with a quiet grin,
Cos you've realised in a moment

That the place you were is gone forever—
It's now no more than the place you've been.

Seize the day,
Grab the moment,
This one is yours,
A chance is a gift
That no one ignores!

I'm taking mine; I'm going all the way,
A promise made on this very day.

Happiness is the journey—
What are you waiting for?

Get on your way,
Never give up!

STAR

Blink for a moment as you glance at a star,
Take a moment to realise; this is where you are.
Watch the light as it dances before you,
Twinkling forever, so far above.

It's a mystery that I've begun to love.
With a billion miles between us and its glow,
Reach out and touch it, you know you can;
Just being able to see it makes you a much stronger man!

Go on and feel it, say that you can;
Space is as vast as the human mind;
It calls to us all because we're humankind.

FINDING YOU

A wise man once told me: the first cut is the deepest.
In reality, it's only as deep as you make it yourself.

Though many of my wounds are apparent, most are never seen.

The depth that I've known is beyond me now, but sadly still
lies before many.

Can we heal our wounds with selfless fun,
Can we end our pain with hopeless gain?

Each of us dreams as each of us hopes,
Take a chance with your life simply because you can.

Find your dreams, make a plan;
Find yourself, you know you can!

HELP HIM LIVE

Silent dreams pass him by;
He's hurt and lost, and yet so shy.

His heart is bleeding, as alone I cry.

He sits alone with his eternal goodbye,
Dreaming of hope, but waking to pain;
Waiting on sunshine, whilst surrounded by rain.

Can you feel it, do you think the same?

Take a moment if you can to let his fear take hold,
Its agony in full will never be told;
He's always lost, his heart was sold.

Feel the chill, now on your burning face,
As through a broken mind, you find your place.

Surely, he knows his pain will ease;
His heart is cold; it's beginning to freeze.

Pity his pain as you feel his disease;
Make him know, help him see,
Give him the knowledge to set him free,

Pain comes and goes, but this life is yours!

Know it.

DAD

Here's a few words that aren't always said. My hope is they'll mean something once they are read . . .

When I think of you and all that you've done, I see what someday I hope to become, and I'm proud to be my father's son. My earliest memories are filled with the places you took me and the times we had, from the lighthouse at Hughs to the Port Giles Jetty. I didn't ever say it near enough, but I even remember that Tommy Rough. With a simple act, you gave me a gift: you taught me to love. You taught me to live, and your loving nature has taught me to give.

The days become years, but time can't deny the memories of a bluffing pretender . . . the time you created the banana bender!

You've worked your hands to the bone, and we see the proof; it's more than our house, our walls, our roof. It's morals I've learned by watching your ways. My love is with you till the end of days.

STEVE IRWIN

The endless life of an eternal heart brings hope to an empty soul.

Smiles fade on the faces of millions as nature's warrior left the unspoilt earth that alone was his; the passion he knew will bring life's emptiness to an end, as the gift he gave is ours to keep and mend.

His final stand was for our own good;
The strongest will follow his path;
They know they should.

With a khaki top and Aussie shorts,
This is the man who inspires our thoughts.

Our debt to Steve before we leave is to follow the path his life has bought.

With the strength of thousands,
Not one can ignore us.

To the heavens above, look up with love;
You may feel tiny, you may feel small,
But carried on the wind is a message so cool;
An eternal voice that echoes, "Crocs rule!"

Thank God for the blood that flows the same;
From your darling wife, Terri;
Those lives share your name;
Bindi and Robert Irwin live deep in our hearts;
God bless their gift as they do their part;
One day, they'll share in fighting for nature;
You'll be forever with them, of that, I'd wager.

In Matty's Own Words

Tears fall from heaven with a pain I can't bear;
My pain is my own, but with the world I share.

So, three cheers to the one and only Stevie boy Irwin;
To you, my hero, my mate;
Your message lives on in the hearts of all,
As we shout, "Croc's rule!" and grieve your fate.

Forever missed and a loss deep inside;
Your legacy lives on through the sharing of your pride.

Peace mate, we miss you,
Gibbo.

••5•••

Stop the Downward Spiral

*"Chains of habit are too light to be felt
until they are too heavy to be broken."*

—*Warren Buffet*

FORMING A HABIT is like watching a plant grow. All seeds take root and sprout upward towards their reward: the warmth of the sun. At this new growth stage, just like the weeds that usually grow alongside, they can easily be pulled out.

When we want to form new habits, we need to nurture the growth by allowing the roots to go deep over time. Once the seeds develop deep roots, it is much harder to pull out the plant or break the habit. The same is true for the bad habits we tend to nurture, just because it is easier to let them grow.

I see this every day in my garden at home. Weeds sprout up alongside my veggie plants, and if I remove them straight away, it's all good. However, if I leave them to establish themselves, they are almost impossible to extract. Not only are they tough to pull out at the site of the growth, but I often find their roots have spread insidiously into many other parts of the garden.

The same goes for our bad habits. They may seem harmless at first but over time cause problems in other areas of our lives and are very hard to break once they have rooted deeply. Very hard doesn't mean impossible. Knowing the triggers or cues that precede our habits is a great place to start working on change.

THREE PHASES OF HABIT-FORMING

Habits form in three stages.

1. Cue: Our brain works in such a way that we can learn to be cued without even realising it. This is how we are hacked by social media, for example, to look at our devices as often as possible.
2. Routine: When we are in the habit of a reward, we naturally perform the same routine once we are cued to do so.
3. Reward: Receiving the reward is what habituates the routine.

A great example of this is our behaviour when watching a program on television; an advert that comes on is our cue, then getting up and going to the fridge becomes our routine. We then enjoy a great snack or drink, which is the reward. The key to changing habits is to identify our cues, then becoming aware and more intentional with our routine and reward. It takes intention in the beginning because the routine often happens on autopilot.[39]

THE BRAIN AND HABITS

Our habit-making behaviours begin in a section of the brain called the basal ganglia, which also plays a significant role in the development of emotions, memories, and pattern recognition. Neuroscientists have discovered that decisions are made elsewhere in the brain: the prefrontal cortex. However, as soon as a behaviour becomes automatic, the decision-making part of our brain isn't required, so we go into autopilot mode. This can be a good thing if the habit is a positive one, as it saves using unnecessary energy.

Our habits become imprinted onto the brain through neural pathways, which is why they are hard to break. Repetition with intention is key in forming new helpful habits.

A SIMPLE STRATEGY TO CHANGE HARMFUL HABITS

Let's talk about *habits that harm* us and lead to a life of anxiety and indecision. We've all developed habits, but it's the ones that lead to adverse changes in our lives that we need to interrupt. Do we get into the habit of hesitating every time we have a great idea, doubt our ability to get it done? Do we worry about all the things that could go wrong? Instead of jumping straight in and putting our vision into action, we lose focus, we get hacked by fear, and the idea stagnates. Do this enough times, and it becomes a *habit that harms*. We live a life in agitation, our brain is stressing, and we get caught in the never-ending loop of procrastination. Anxiety sets in because we can't make up our mind, we're not accomplishing anything, we start using negative self-talk, and it's all downhill from there. I know you can relate. We've all been there and maybe still are.

Three simple words can change all that: UP UNTIL NOW. Next time you feel yourself hesitate or fear taking action, interrupt the negative thought process with UP UNTIL NOW, I didn't take action, but I know I will, and then DO IT. That's the key: jump straight in once you commit.[40]

We need to interrupt the habit of negativity, then take action continually. Interrupt the old thought, replace it with a new and positive idea, then take action. When done enough times, this strategy replaces bad habits with good ones. Taking action also alleviates anxiety. We need to stop overthinking. Start anywhere; imperfect action is better than no action and is a great starting point. Once you make the decision, the pressure will go. You feel in control, and that's a great feeling.

There will always be problems in life we cannot control, but when we are in charge of our actions and responses, we win every time.

Science proves that with repetition, we develop a bias toward action, and it becomes more comfortable each time. Changing your thought process and your harmful habits is a win-win exercise.

Our subconscious mind is awake 24/7 and runs on habit. Neuroscience proves that by changing our brain's pathways, we can be confident of a productive, happier life with very little anxiety.

SAVVY MARKETING

These days, good marketers study our habits, and we find ourselves being hacked at every turn. For example, during special occasions when our emotions are high, we are more susceptible to suggestions from marketers about purchasing certain items. Have you ever fallen into this trap? I sure have.

Birthdays, weddings, baby showers—all the exciting life events that raise our emotions also raise the attention of savvy marketers. Because our habits, likes, and dislikes are all tracked on social media under the guise of providing us with the best and latest information pertaining to our needs, it can have a detrimental effect on our mental health. It's overwhelming much of the time, and something has to give, usually our mental health, hence the importance of becoming aware and taking good care of our mind and body.

I think the answer to this can only come down to mindfulness, similar to becoming more aware of how we interact on social media and what habits we have formed. What we focus our mind on is the key to what we unlock in life. As I teach with the *Unhackable* message, we must choose our inputs with deliberate focus. We need to know what it is we want and put our own ideas into practise. Experiencing *unhackability* is the best way to reach our goals and fulfil our dreams. Learning how to be in flow as we move toward achieving our goals is life-changing.

ANXIETY

A number of habits are known as nervous habits which stem from anxiety. These include nail-biting, repetitive sniffling, stammering, and banging the head. These habits generally stem from emotions which negatively impact our lives: feelings of inferiority, insecurity, and tension, to name a few. These habits are often formed at a young age, and many believe they stem from a need for attention. I don't believe it matters why we develop these habits, especially when it's said it stems from childhood. We just need to know how to modify the behaviour in our best interest now. Always thinking positively is a great first step.

When trying to overcome a nervous habit, it is important to resolve the cause of the nervous emotion rather than the symptom. Relying purely on willpower won't do it. It's the never-ending cycle again; the stronger the habit, the more we worry, then anxiety increases, and the habit sets in. It's very important to find the cause and start looking to remedy it there. Replacing the habit with a healthier coping mechanism is a great idea. For example, you could use a squeeze ball every time you are tempted to bite your nails. Your body gets the reward, or pay off, and you keep your nails—win-win!

DECADES OF KNOWLEDGE QUESTIONED

We punish people who struggle with addiction by trying to make them conform to our way of thinking. How bold we are to assume we have all the answers without walking a step in their shoes. If you have ever loved someone who is addicted or someone who depends on alcohol to get through the day, then you will know first-hand the anguish they suffer. You will know of the time they spend alone agonising over what they have done, desperately trying to get back to normal. Unfortunately, most of what we know about addiction is outdated.

I can confidently say this because the problem is becoming more significant in society, and I have lived through loving someone while trying all of what society had taught me on the subject. It is not a choice; it's a trap. The more we pushed using these known methods, over the years, things progressively got worse. Something had to change.

Matty believed he had the answer and was on the path to making it work. I think Matty had the right approach to healing himself, and he badly wanted to share that knowledge and experience with other sufferers.

Recently, when I was in the hospital with a severe gall bladder attack, the doctor administered morphine to control the pain. Morphine is heroin. When we break bones, morphine is the painkiller; it is used routinely in modern medicine, always without patients becoming addicted. I actually didn't realise this was such a strong drug, but the fact that addiction doesn't happen when we use painkillers during illness really interested me once I read about drug experiments using lab rats.

Back in the 1960s, experiments on drug-taking using lab rats produced a set of results that formed a basis for all we know about addiction. Experimenters offered heroin laced water and plain water to rats who lived in an empty cage. The rats used heroin water much more and increased their use until they became ill and died. The professors must have felt thrilled at their results, and with the much-publicised findings, these types of studies formed societies view that drugs are entirely addictive and lethal. In the decades previous to these findings, the world firmly believed demons possessed people who had a substance use disorder. That seems incredible, but as a result, the treatment of these poor souls became increasingly inhumane.

As the years went on, and as a result of these experiments, we, as a society, formed very biased attitudes and treated those whose lives had spiralled out of control very poorly.

Sadly, we now know that rats are very social creatures, and these tests were carried out with rats in isolation. A very different outcome was about to be found.[41]

RAT PARK

In recent years, I had the pleasure of corresponding with Doctor Bruce Alexander, professor of psychology. He answered my questions and kindly sent me pages of his research to answer my many other questions. His life's work has been on the problems the world faces due to addiction, and his knowledge on this subject and his compassion for humanity is outstanding. His particular interest is in the causes of all kinds of addiction and how to stop it.

Using all the previous reports, he began his own set of experiments. He, too, found that animals who were isolated drank the heroin water to their detriment. History has proved the fact that during wars, isolation is a form of torture or punishment. Bruce Alexander questioned the first findings when he put everything into this perspective. Were the isolated rats feeling disconnected, lost, and alone? Did they drink the heroin to escape their situation, and not because of any hook or desperate need? He had to test his theories. His first experiment using rats in isolation yielded similar results, then he began to make a change to prove his theory.

Back in the seventies, he built the most beautiful rat home called "Rat Park" to test drug use on a whole new level. An entire community of rats inhabited the park. They had playmates, partners, family, clean water, food, toys, tunnels, shelter, and every comfort to produce a happy life. Everything the rats needed for their heart's content was in this park along with two lots of water: one pure water and one laced with heroin. Bruce Alexander discovered that rats are very gregarious little animals; in fact, they are a lot like humans in their basic needs and behaviours. The rats rarely used heroin water when they had everything needed to feel connected and happy in their lives. They never became addicted and never overdosed. As the days and weeks passed, the excitement in that room must have been palpable. Bruce mentioned that with these results, he believed everything would change in the way we viewed addiction; help was at hand to ease the suffering of millions.[42]

Personally, when I heard of these results, I, too, was ecstatic! By his writings, I knew Matthew held similar views. Matty believed that amongst other things, we needed change, connection, and adventure to overcome these debilitating habits. His plan of action to help those who struggle did indeed include all three. I was truly amazed and thankful to read of the success of these experiments because I knew they gave life to Matty's beliefs.

You might be asking yourself why we haven't all heard about these notable findings, and why nothing has changed over the decades. I, too, needed to know and delved much more in-depth.

THE DISAPPOINTMENT

Doctor Bruce Alexander set about attracting funding to continue these promising experiments. If the rats didn't become addicted to heroin, then was it indeed society that needed to change their outlook to stop this insidious problem and not the other way around? Was there more to this subject? Should we lay the blame squarely on the shoulders of those addicted? No, clearly not. So much needed to be answered. Working at Simon Fraser University meant that funding was a must to continue any experiment. Bruce Alexander and his colleagues excitedly set about this quest. History now shows that funds were not forthcoming, and the university had no choice but to close down the experiment, despite the promise it offered. Sadly, this is the way of the world. No money, no deal.[43]

I personally believe the funding was not forthcoming because of the preconceived ideas we hold onto so firmly in many aspects of life. In the space of a few short decades, we had gone from the belief that drug users were demon-possessed to the blind and unproven idea that drugs contained addicting chemicals which after one use would hook individuals for life. Once an idea takes hold, individuals are often determined to keep it.

Maybe I'm cynical, but I see this every day in my Bible study, so it's not such a far cry to imagine it happens in other walks of life. The Bible tells us to search out the matter on all things concealed; it is the honour of kings to search it out. Not only kings but all of us should be searching for Bible truth. Originally written in Hebrew and Greek, the Bible is a mystery to many. Because it was translated into English with preconceived ideas in mind, it causes much of the texts meaning to be hidden. It's up to us to search out the matter. I have studied the original Hebrew and Greek for forty-five years. I use a concordance to check for clues, context, consistency, cross-references, and clarity to discover the true meaning of the verses. It's thrilling to see and read the Bible as God intended us to know it, not as man has tried to manipulate it. Perhaps you are aware of similar areas in your life where things are not as they seem?

Bruce Alexander was unable to convince funders that drugs might not be as addictive as we thought and that those who struggle may do so for other reasons. The old, set in stone beliefs held firm.

His research was a real breakthrough and should have continued for the sake of all humanity. The fact that funding was not forthcoming does not mean the study wasn't valuable.

THE TRUTH OF THE MATTER

Because of this downward spiral that occurs as an effect of a varied list of issues, we must take great care to pay attention to the first sign of this. If due care, support, and understanding don't occur, then a retreat into isolation and a further downward spiral can occur. It's in this place that I believe is a breeding ground for negative habits to form as a coping mechanism.

There is also the fact that personalities, life experiences, and genetic factors also come into play. Some individuals are more vulnerable than others. Individuals who suffer mental health issues are fifty percent more likely to struggle with a substance use disorder. They need our support!

A LETTER FROM BRUCE ALEXANDER

Understandably, Doctor Alexander was devastated by the news that his experiment had to be closed. The good news was that he was able to continue his studies in other forms, so over many years, he contributed much to the world's knowledge, which I believe will one day change how we view addictions.

I wrote to Bruce again, asking him further questions regarding any changes over the years, and the following was his response:

Hello again, Karen,

I am attaching a paper that I put on my website in 2017, at a time when I was experiencing considerable despair about the lack of real progress in the field of addiction, despite all the wonderful people who truly understand what is going on and trying hard to change things. This, I think, would be my answer to the question that you posed to me in your email a few days ago. I wish you all good luck and Godspeed on finishing your book. I will be sure to read it (especially if you all let me know when it is going to be published).

Best Wishes,
Bruce Alexander

ENVIRONMENT AND HABIT

Over the years, Bruce Alexander's life work produced more critical information on this subject. Now in his eighties, he is retired, but I believe we owe him a debt of gratitude.

We have another example documented around the same time as Doctor Alexander's experiment: the Vietnam war. Around a quarter of the soldiers were using drugs, and authorities believed there would be an epidemic of addiction once the soldiers returned home. The American Journal of Public Health did a detailed study on this and discovered ninety-five per cent of the soldiers simply stopped using once home.[44] Surprisingly, the expected withdrawals and rehab admissions didn't happen. Doctor Alexander was intrigued.

God created us to bond and connect with each other. He did not intend human beings to be alone. Doctor Alexander's experiments proved that if deprived of connection, everyday interaction, and the chance to bond or connect, then we will bond with something else to bring relief to our disconnected environment. He studied many cultures in his quest for answers, and there is much evidence to support this theory. He lives in Canada, so he cites the Canadian natives as an example. Here in Australia, we see the example in our Aboriginal population. Once displaced from their natural environment, their culture, and all they knew, depression and addiction became rife. Many other cultures bear witness to this fact.

For most of us, if we could not bear to be present in our current situation, if we felt depressed and had no connection, we would bond elsewhere. It's a downward spiral made up of a series of events that could be prevented. We were created to be present and to excel, not to be isolated and alone, but we still tend to punish and shame those struggling with addiction.

Worst of all, we isolate them. The barriers we erect make it almost impossible for them to reconnect, so the downward spiral continues into a much deeper decline.

Our whole society is vulnerable to addictions: to our phones, other devices, the internet, etc. As a society, we are lonelier than ever, hence the increase in addictive behaviours.

We all need something to keep us going—some on a small scale some on a large, but the most important thing is to show love and support to our loved ones who are struggling with mental health issues and worse.

Increased drug use is an escape from life for many people. Many individuals are not scared of dying; they are afraid to live. Mental health issues, bullying, extreme anxiety, failed relationships, and low self-esteem lead to isolation, leaving a person open and exposed to depression and the subsequent downward spiral. It's time we did something different to support our loved ones.

Never forget your divine birth right. You've been created to create, and when you do, you're literally fulfilling your God-given calling.

—Kary Oberbrunner

Part 3
EMBRACING A BRIGHTER FUTURE

• • • | • • •

Destiny

"Destiny is a name often given in retrospect
to choices that had dramatic consequences."
—JK Rowling

CONNECTING

THOUGH I DON'T feel that enabling is the appropriate term to always use when we're supporting our loved ones, maybe, just maybe, there is such a thing if the downward spiral has taken a deep hold.

The difference between support and enabling is a question I come across so often. In writing this book, I have deeply pondered the reason for my aversion to considering supporters enablers.

I've concluded, those who use this term are often confused. The stigmas held by many regarding mental health cause us to feel that we are supposed to force sufferers to stand on their own two feet. It's as though this is the end goal, so right from the beginning, our treatment of our loved ones must reflect the end goal.

Here's where I feel the truth lies.

Living life on purpose, happily, and in a productive manner is the ultimate goal; however, this does not magically happen. It's a long process, and support is needed to arrive at the destination.

I knew a family who had a loved one struggling with her mental health for many years, and indeed, she had sadly fallen into the downward spiral of substance use disorder.

If you have a loved one going through this, then you know the trials involved. It is not an easy road to walk. It is painful for the entire family and completely disrupts life.

You must remember one thing: it is not a choice. Substance Use Disorder (SUD) is even more painful and traumatic for the one caught in the trap as it is for the rest of the family. Sometimes, we forget this fact. We see our loved one behaving erratically, disrupting the family, causing all sorts of grief, and we often become angry. We view the person as the problem, when, in fact, it's the disorder. Your loved one is still there, struggling underneath the symptoms.

Consider the example of the young woman I spoke of earlier. She had gone through this struggle. Her family were at their wit's end. She had been in rehab twice, and both times, she had relapsed.

Her family were enjoying a meal and catching up when she came out of rehab for the third time. What would you do at this time? The exact moment to show support has now arrived!

Sadly, this family thought they needed to send her away to stand on her own two feet to prove she wasn't going to relapse again. If you take anything away from this book, let it be that you always show support and reward the small steps. Push out the stigmas that might colour your mind. Look at the facts in this case: this young woman was doing her best, and she had tried three times to overcome her struggles. At that very moment, she was clean and sober, so wouldn't it follow that this is the time to embrace her, give thanks for her healing, and encourage her to stay on this path of health and hope? Draw her into the family celebration and let her feel loved, wanted, and accepted. Show her the life she could have and the support she needs to stay on her chosen path of healing; this goes a long way to cementing the need to keep clean.

With a strong show of support, she would have had a much higher chance of success. To push her away at this vulnerable time is like saying, "You've failed twice, so it's most likely you will fail again." Why would we do this to someone we love just because we are *told* not to enable? We are actually doing the opposite; we allow our loved one to go out there alone, to feel isolated, seeking solace in substance.

The term *enabling* has caused so much confusion and ultimately more harm than good. Not every situation is the same, but a golden rule is to reward progress and always assume the best. The term, *enabling*, should never be used in relation to depression and anxiety.

We all need to feel supported and know we are loved. Encouragement goes a long way in winning this fight. It cannot possibly do any good to push someone who has just come through a traumatic ordeal and most likely feeling vulnerable to prove their worth. Show love and belief in this situation and keep your loved one close.

Matty and I believe there is always hope. I'm encouraging you to support your loved one through depression and anxiety, and keep them close to you, their family, and all they hold dear. Preventing the downward spiral starts here.

Twice during Matty's early struggles, I was told by doctors *not to enable him.* They were, in effect, telling me to isolate him to *get over it* on his own. At that time, he was taking prescription medication, which only made matters worse.

I thank God every day I didn't take heed. The second time, I almost did because nothing seemed to be working, and it's not easy for the one struggling or those who love them.

We hadn't found the answers at that stage, and I wondered if we were on the right track. It might appear to be easier to let go, but easier doesn't mean better.

On that second occasion, I struggled with the advice. I had always believed doctors knew so much more than I, but that attitude changed years before when the mistake of a doctor almost cost my older son his life. The doctor had not opened an x-ray report but had diagnosed my eldest boy with asthma. For years, his condition progressively worsened until in desperation I begged that they do more tests. Long story short, it turned out he never had asthma, but as showed on the earlier x-ray, he had a collapsed lung due to pneumonia. Due to the time it remained collapsed, he developed *bronchiectasis*, and part of his lung had to be surgically removed. This changed my entire perspective.

Doctors are only human; they are not infallible and will follow the current information on any health issue. Much of the advice available on mental health issues result in the isolation of the person struggling, which goes against my natural nurturing personality but also my common sense. I didn't know any better at the time, but I knew I loved my son Matty, and it felt right to stay connected with love and support. I went with my gut and am eternally thankful for that decision. Always trust your gut, continue to reward the small steps forward, and be present as a companion and witness in their struggle. Flawed advice, no matter how well intentioned, never helps.

LOVE COMMITMENT

It takes love and commitment to follow through, but the result is worth it. Individuals who struggle with their mental health are often hard to be around, but knowing their often-negative attitude can and will change in time is the big WHY to keep going. Life throws us some mighty tough curve balls sometimes, but what if we dropped the ball each and every time? We'd never learn and never grow. I used to wonder why this was happening to my family and to myself. Everyone else seemed to be getting ahead in life, and their kids seemed happy and healthy. I felt depressed myself and so sad I couldn't heal Matty. I loved him, though, more than my life and still do. He appreciated that love and tried his best to recover. No matter what he went through, Matty never gave up, and that means something.

Matty had a way to go, but when he passed away from this life, he was still trying his best. He hadn't accomplished his dream of connecting with other sufferers to help them heal, but with the plans laid out, his life and message have still changed so many lives for the better. He was on track, but who knows where he might have been if I had heeded negative advice from people who would suffer no pain with the outcome? In a far worse place, I'd guess, because some things in life can be a living death, a place where there would seem to be no hope. I thank God for His mercies every day.

MATTY'S LETTER

Earlier that fateful year, I was sick in bed with bronchitis and asthma. Matty brought me a letter that he had written on one of his self-development worksheets. On the top was printed: "The things that I will gain from staying in recovery are:" Matty had printed "LIFE."

Then underneath, he wrote me this letter:

Please stay strong, my darling mother. We are a family, and we're always together. No matter what, you have never turned your back, though I've put you through hell. No more hell, babe. Happy days and smiles, no matter what. You and our amazing family are my rock; I want to be yours now. Get well soon, bub.

All my love, your
Matty Man
xxxx Love you all xxx

It's these moments that make everything worthwhile. Looking back now, I am so thankful to have this letter and so grateful at the way we worked through everything. It's the reason I want to encourage you to stay connected, to never give up, and to show love and support, for the payoff is huge. You have to live with every decision you make, so make them good ones. None of us knows when our time is up; every day has to count.

FACE THE FUTURE WITH LOVE

We can't pretend our loved one isn't suffering and simply put it out of our mind. It won't go away on its own. It's another of life's many turmoils we have to overcome. It's an age-old fact that positivity breeds positivity. Your attitude will rub off on your loved one, and their very life depends on it. Matty and I helped each other through life. I did my very best for him, and the steps he took toward improvement along with the love he showed our family will be with me always. My gut told me to do the opposite of what the doctor said, and I feel eternally grateful to God that the strength I took from Him enabled me to trust my gut and place my hope and faith in Him.

···2···

The Ultimate Key to Healing

"Nature is my manifestation of God."
—Frank Lloyd Wright

ADVENTURE

A STRONG CONNECTION is the key to healing. What better way to connect than to share an adventure? Matty realised that the further people withdrew, the worse their symptoms would become. It's sometimes easier to be alone and not have to keep on trying. People who struggle with depression often find it exhausting to keep pushing through. The trick is to be aware of the need for rest but to be intentional with making progress. When struggling with depression, the sufferer needs lots and lots of rest. Taking time out to rest isn't the same as withdrawing or becoming isolated. It's essential to recognise the difference.

Planning an adventure was something Matty decided to do to help himself, as well as a group of others who struggled with depression. He had talked about his idea with some friends and asked my opinion on his plan.

I knew it was a good idea but felt apprehensive as to the danger involved in such an undertaking. To raise money for the plan to work, Matty had to think of something that would gain attention. He was right in that. People tend to pay more attention if something is risky; strange but true. Matty had the courage, but I, as his mother, could only think of the dangers. I deeply regret that now; I was always so bent on protecting those I loved. Taking risks seemed out of the question, but Matty believed that *connection* through *adventure* was the ultimate key to healing, and his thoughts turned to the ocean.

THE GREAT BARRIER REEF

Just waiting to be explored in the vastly magnificent Coral Sea, off Australia's East Coast, lies the world's most extensive coral reef system. You possibly know it as the Great Barrier Reef. Dotted across 2,300 kilometres of the Pacific Ocean is over 900 islands surrounded by thousands of individual reefs. It's a wonder to behold and lies in our back yard.

Matty first dreamed of sharing this wonder with the world to raise money for those in need of adventure.

The entire reef system covers over 344,000 square kilometres which, to put into perspective, is larger than the United Kingdom, Switzerland, and Holland combined. The Great Barrier Reef Marine Park is a complex natural eco-system which includes hundreds of continental islands, coral cays, and in-shore mangrove islands, so it's not hard for the imagination to run wild.

Matty had the idea of making a documentary of an adventure from one of the atolls on the Great Barrier Reef. Atolls are rings of coral that create protected lagoons in the middle of the ocean. Fishing boats will often make for the atolls if caught in a sudden storm or if they plan to stay overnight to fish the next day. The protection they provide is uniquely dependable.

Matty planned on finding sponsorship to film the whole adventure to produce a documentary to raise money for youth depression and substance dependency. He was such a funny person and jokingly wrote to ask a friend to help, saying, "I need a cameraman/fishing guru, fearless, or just plain dumb passenger, lol. The only thing I know for sure at the moment is that it will happen . . . the journey starts here :)"

He wrote "plain dumb" as a joke because he intended to do this from a small five-metre tinny, making it dangerous. His point was that it had to be different from other documentaries to get people's attention. Matty contacted a friend who appeared in a well-known fishing show to see if they'd like to get involved with sponsorship. He planned on catching giant dogtooth tuna, sharks, coral trout, and crayfish by diving and fishing from this tiny boat while living on the outer edge of the reef for a week.

The second plan he had was to travel down the East Coast of Australia in his canoe—another dangerous undertaking. In April 2015, he wrote to all his friends:

Hi, I'm planning a pretty dangerous canoe ride into shark-infested waters. I want to make and see a difference in the lives of young people. I see too many kids on drugs and too many young lads on the bottle. Teen and adult depression is at an all-time high; I've been there for years, and it is one of my dreams to live this out while helping others at the same time. It's a win-win. I'll be registering a charity, and everyone who pledges twenty dollars or more will receive a copy of the DVD and a say in where the money goes. Please contact me if you can help. It's for all of us.

Kind regards,
Matt Gibbs

The previous year, Matty had landed a giant Barramundi from his canoe which renewed his determination and caught the interest of the media.

This photo and accompanying half-page story made it into the *Sunshine Coast Daily*, entitled "Now That's a Barramundi! Matt's Biggest Catch Yet." Even in this interview, Matty used his words to help others instead of basking in his moment of glory. The half-page story outlined his catch and detailed how he managed such an amazing feat from his tiny canoe but also mentioned the fact that it was Matts tentative step back to the life he thrived on before a series of failed relationships led to a battle with alcohol in recent years. The writer, Bill Hoffman, wrote:

> The story of this fish is about more than a great catch well eaten and put on display. It is really about a young bloke who loved the ocean, fishing and diving but who lost his way. Matt's mum's advice to "get back to what you love and

you'll be rewarded" is also not about a fish but a chance to recapture a life that made him happy. It's a simple axiom he wants others who have found themselves in his situation to consider. He's convinced that while he has a way to go, now, having felt the tug and the adrenaline rush, he is back on the right path.

Barra inhale the water with their prey, making a sound like a woo-oof. For Matt in a small canoe on a starry night, it can sound like coming home to a life thought lost.[45]

MEMORIES SHAPE US

Life is a risk, and progress is a risk, just as staying stuck in one spot is a risk. Possibly the latter is the most significant risk of all. I know that now. Thinking back, I realise, Matty had always been keen about the ocean because our family centred every holiday around the sea and fishing. His skill was unique. He loved nature so intently that he seemed to have learned all there was to know about the sea, fishing, and boating. I knew he was planning on using his memories to make new ones with people who needed something on which to hope.

I understand why this was so important to Matty. He had such unforgettable memories that sustained him during the hard times. He wanted others to feel this joy and to make their own set of memories. Matty knew people who struggled with their mental health needed to be supported to get out into nature because it is always easier to withdraw or retreat, which is never the answer. He had a knack of supporting others in such a way that they didn't feel lacking or hopeless in their lives. His support gave them the confidence to step up and heal. It's that first important step without pressure that makes all the difference.

We reminisced about all the memories we had made as he continued to dream and plan. I am extremely thankful for the time I was blessed to share with Matty and all that he taught me.

DUNK ISLAND

Matty vividly remembered one trip to Dunk Island, four kilometres off the coast of Queensland. It's beautiful memories like these Matty wanted to share with others but not just in the telling. Matty wanted to share the experiences with others in need of adventure.

Filled with excitement, he could hardly wait to arrive. Matty knew all about the species of fish in those waters, and he was sure he would catch some barramundi and spangled emperor. I think he was only about thirteen or fourteen at the time.

After arriving in Mission Beach on the beautiful Cassowary Coast, we settled into our overnight accommodation before arranging for a minibus to take us to the waterfront the next morning. We parked the Land Cruiser safely for when we returned the following week.

The morning dawned warm and bright, and we could taste the salty ocean carried to us on a brisk wind. Outside, we spotted a large adult cassowary, unique to this area. With its large beady eyes and grey casque on its head, looking for all the world like a helmet, it reminded me of a prehistoric creature. A bright red wattle hung from its bald, blue neck as it strutted along as though it owned the place. I guess it did in a way, as they are a protected species. Its long black feathers looked more like hair. It was both beautiful and menacing to behold.

Upon arriving at the waterfront, we saw a small rickety jetty which looked none too safe. The boat was there rising and falling with the swell of the ocean. We were helped aboard by the deckhands, who definitely had their work cut out for them. The ladder on the side of the boat seemed to be moving as much as the ocean. Finally settled aboard, we headed across the sea. The boat rose high over the giant swell. Afraid of motion sickness, I kept my eyes focused on the horizon. Although the surges carried the boat high, it was nonetheless smooth. Arriving without incident, I remember feeling quite perturbed when I saw the island jetty. The deckhands were out first to help the passengers alight. The large swell was causing the boat the rise and fall at the edge of the wooden pylons. To my eyes, the boat was neither close enough to the jetty nor stable enough to be able to get off.

When my turn came to climb the ladder, I balanced precariously, and each time I went to step off, the boat would rise what felt like four feet higher. The deckhands were trying to hold the boat as close as possible with the aid of thick coiled ropes. "Jump, Mumma!" Matty shouted. *Jump? Is he kidding me?* I thought. Oh, how we laughed at that particular memory. I counted the rhythm in my head and did indeed jump as the boat came down on the swell. I felt like a wrung-out dishcloth and wanted to recover, but Matty was keen to go fishing, so fishing it was.

THE HEADLAND

Once at the water, Matty wanted to go around the headland to fish. Climbing rocks was not my thing, and I was also concerned, as the ocean was none too smooth.

Matty told me he knew what to do, and he'd be back for dinner. Time went on as the water rose higher over the rocks, and there was still no sign of Matty. I began to feel anxious when the water started to cover the sandy path on the corner Matty had rounded. We called for help to find Matty. The island staff said the rising tide would soon cover the way around the headland, and dusk was upon us. Now, I was frantic! At that moment, Matty appeared, clambering over the rocks just above the high-water line. I heaved a sigh of relief.

As usual, Matty knew precisely what time the tide would be in and how much time he had. Looking back, I realise his knowledge of the ocean far surpassed mine. He was never in any danger and felt quite miffed I doubted him. Oh, the joys of motherhood!

BIG BARRA

The next day, Matty's skills would come to the fore once again. While fishing on the jetty, he said, "I'm going to catch a big barra," short for Barramundi, a very delicious and sought-after fish. He set about preparing his line and hook with whatever it is one uses to catch barra. Clearly, I don't fish.

Into the deep, he cast, and within a short time, he was on. He played his line with skill. "Go slow, let it run, keep the pressure on, pump and wind!" I don't know if that's how he played this particular fish, but he often said this phrase when teaching anyone, so it's what always comes to my mind when I think of fishing. A considerable time later, he landed the monster on the jetty. It was a giant barra 18 kilos and around 800 cm. I wasn't surprised. If Matty said he was aiming to catch a particular species, he always did.

Two young men came walking up the jetty with their fishing rods in hand. They looked incredulously at the fish and asked where it came from. Silly question, but it turned out, they had lived on the island for the past year and had fished that jetty every night to try to catch a barra. They asked how long we'd been on the island and were doubly astounded when we said we'd just arrived!

At the time, I thought Matty had a natural talent, but looking back, I see he had an extraordinary gift. Some years later, in 2014, he caught the giant barra that got his story in the paper. He had a fantastic talent and was so right to want to use that gift to support others.

I have a Facebook page of our Aussie travels. It's just for fun, but if you'd like to share some of the sights with us, check out my website.

THE PLAN

Matty formulated a plan in his mind. He understood the needs of those who struggled and knew this connection would make all the difference. His idea was to take five people who struggled with depression on an adventure. He believed the type of experiences he had enjoyed in his life were to be shared and would be life-changing for many. Matty planned to use all his skills and knowledge but seek medical professionals to oversee the health of the participants. He drafted a letter to seek outside support and planned to approach Australia Zoo along with other contacts he already had.

As I write this now, I remember him outlining the plan to me, and my initial thought was it was too big an undertaking. It seemed like climbing a mountain! I didn't doubt, though, that if anyone could climb that mountain, it would be Matty.

THE IDEA

Here is the first partial draft of his idea, an attempt to put his thoughts, ideas, and dreams onto paper:

Hi, my name is Matt, and I'm trying to raise funds to purchase a life-changing gift that I plan to use solely for charity. After spending some time in the mental health ward at Nambour Hospital, suffering from depression and alcohol misuse, it occurred to me that the only help available is counselling help-lines, drugs to calm you, drugs to help you sleep, and the list goes on.

*Alcohol misuse, depression, and youth suicide are steadily ris-
ing, and our new generation suffers in silence every day. People
are throwing their lives away because they think they have no
purpose, no love. Some are alcoholics, some are compulsive gam-
blers, some are hopelessly addicted to drugs, and some feel that
poverty is holding them back. Hence, the only way to cope is to
dull their senses, thus spiralling them deeper into depression.*

*Many of us lead such busy lives that we often overlook the men
and women who so desperately need help.*

*I am twenty-nine years old, and although I am blessed with a
loving family, I suffer daily with depression, gambling addiction, and my dearest mother watching me kill myself one drink
at a time. My mum watched her father die young, and I never
knew him. I know she lives for her family and worries constantly for myself. I can no longer stand by and watch her suffer
in what should be a peaceful time to look on with pride at the
family to which she devoted her life.*

*I want her to be proud of me and to find peace in my happiness.
I am the youngest of four. My brothers and sister are married
and have found peace. Sure, I could quit the drink, give the
gambling away, and get work, as I am lucky enough to be a
qualified wall and floor tiler. I know my mum would be proud,
and I could take my life back for the first time in ten years, but
would I have peace? The answer is no. What peace could I find
knowing others are hopelessly lost?*

To help myself, I intend to help them.

*I cannot free the world, but with a little help, I can start to try.
So, here is my idea! There is a cure—adventure!*

Matty went on to talk about a trip he took to the Solomon Islands, which taught him about the benefits of connection and adventure. Living amongst people who easily survive without the comforts we take for granted, yet never complain, was undoubtedly eye-opening for Matty. Looking at his existence from a different point of view made him realise that although depression and anxiety are severe conditions, they are fixable.

He planned to raise money to take five sufferers on an adventure across Australia that would ultimately change their lives. Matty had mapped out his plan to raise funds and hoped it would turn into a permanent program that if one life could be saved, it would give him peace.

Creating the idea gave him some comfort because he could see the vision; mapped out in his mind, he knew the benefits people in need would find. It was his dream, life goal, and promise to himself. He had a big *why* and didn't allow obstacles to extinguish his dream. He never gave up hope.

···3···

Future Hope

"Hope lies in dreams, in imagination, and in the courage of those who dare to make dreams into reality." —Jonas Salk

WE TOO CAN develop a big *WHY*. Many times, we read quotes and don't honestly think about the meaning, but words have power.

What you focus your mind on is the key to what you unlock in life.

I wrote these words ten years ago; they have come to mean so much more to me today.

If you or your loved one feel stuck in the cycle of negativity, you need to refocus, shake things up, have an adventure, do something different. I have discovered that trying to fix problems day after day, especially if they involve someone else, will only cause you to become stuck in the moment. You can't build a positive life when your mind is full of negativity and worry.

Self-care is important. Remember back to how your RAS filter works? Your brain will look for ways to make your thoughts accurate. Negativity builds negativity. The problems become your total focus and what your life will amount to, a constant pain that could go on in this negative way for years!

It would help if you avoided that continuous cycle of worry and anxiety, where you can't see the wood for the trees. Without strong self-care, you risk being caught in the depressive trap too. When a seemingly unfixable problem is present, we find ourselves caught in a negative loop without realising it. Generating stress by our obsessive desire to fix the problem, we look for quick solutions, only finding momentary relief, but then the worries begin again. We have become a product of negativity. We need to break the cycle, connect with something we love and change the pattern.

Adventure is the key. Refresh your thought process, clear your mind, and the correct answers will come.

MY WHY

I, too, have a big *why*. My story has come full circle. I began this book with the worst day of my life, the day I lost my boy's presence from this life. I will miss him forever and hold him in my heart even longer. His story needed telling; I've been long in the telling because it took an intestinal fortitude that needed developing. It's impossible to even describe the pain I've been through in a way I could hope you'd understand, but that's not important. What's important is that these words fulfil Matty's dream; sure, in a way far different to how he imagined, but still, I pray that many are helped and moved towards healing by the power of these words.

We all have our crosses to bear, and not one of us can hope to escape from pain in this life, but perhaps we can connect, hold each other up, and think of future adventures.

MY STATEMENT OF FAITH

Psalm 56:8 (NLT) reads: "You keep track of all my sorrows. You have collected all my tears in your bottle. You have recorded each one in your book."

Beside this verse in my Bible, I have placed a piece of writing that I mentioned earlier in this book. I call it "My Precious Child."

It is my prayer, my statement of faith, and it is my utmost belief that our loving Heavenly Father hears my plea, because with God, all things are possible if we only believe.

MY PRECIOUS CHILD, MATTHEW

I loved you then; I love you now.

I must learn to live again; I don't know how.

You left me torn when God took your breath,
But He knows best—I know that now.

For a while, you'll sleep in perfect rest,
Something which alluded you in this life,
Although you tried your best.

I will stay the course with a shattered heart,
Until that day that God decreed,
That longed-for day which this world does need.
When things will change, and Christ will come,
To put things right, not only for some.

The whole world will know that Christ is the King,
A King who'll judge with mercy and love,
And bestow His gifts from our Father above.

Future Hope

I will pray for you always until that day,
When before Him, I'll bow in a humble way.
With this hole in my heart, I'll fall at his feet.
He knows my heart and my tears he keeps.
I will plead for the answer to all my prayers.
Plead to be released from this grief I bear.

I will ask that I might hold you again,
That you'll be restored to life,
That your struggle be not in vain.

If through my heartfelt service I might,
On that day, find favour in His sight,
I will thank Him for His gracious gift,
And praise Him forever through thankful lips.

Together we'll worship the God on high,
But for now, I pray that Christ is nigh!

THE END of this part of our story, but for you, my prayer is that it is the beginning of a bigger and better life with a real hope for the future. Read on for further support.

It's a few days until the end of summer. The winds of change will soon announce autumn. I can feel it in the warm, moist air as the days become shorter.

I'm contemplating the past five years on this journey since my life turned upside down.

I, too, can feel a change within myself. I've grown.

The obvious thing to note is that life goes on. While battling grief and depression, I had no choice but to deal with it to accomplish my goals. It feels incredible to have completed this book, bringing Matty's message to the world to leave a lasting legacy. I know how happy this would make him, because although his life was often fraught with turmoil, his heart and hope never wavered. I hope I, too, can say that when my days are done.

How about you? Do you ever feel:

- overwhelmed
- distracted
- frustrated
- plagued by indecision

When was the last time you felt clarity? Are you focused, productive, accomplishing your goals, and living your own unique life to the fullest?

I spent a couple of years absorbing, learning, and surrounding myself with positive people who supported and encouraged my growth to become a certified facilitator, speaker, coach, and trainer.

I empower individuals to feel connected and positively impact the lives of others.

Do you need to:

- find clarity
- achieve your goals

- live a life of purpose
- connect in a meaningful way to family and friends

I learned that we need to acknowledge our pain and understand our own story before helping our loved ones find their way. If you need to find answers, I'd love to support you on this journey we call life.
www.KarenGibbs.com.au
www.linktr.ee/KarenGibbs

STOP THE DOWNWARD SPIRAL

In my custom coaching program, we go deep with powerful sessions around three priorities:

* Connection
* Self-Care
* Transformational Results

Learn how to *Stop the Downward Spiral.* Depression and anxiety can affect the person suffering as well as those who love them. With support, you will transform and be empowered to discover joy once more.

SUPPORT

- Communication
- Conversations that get results
- Connection

TRANSFORM

- Feel heard and understood
- Focus on strengths and coping strategies
- Empower yourself to create the next best step

DISCOVER

- Create a safe space
- Stop judgements
- Alleviate isolation

SHINE

- Understand why loss presents in many forms, and grief is often the result
- Know how to avoid loss of self and the associated grief
- Learn how to pour into yourself with self-care techniques

You will be equipped to effectively manage the stressors of coping with depression and anxiety. You and your loved one will experience the lifechanging results you've been seeking and feel a deeper connection which will lead to healing and a life of purpose.

Email: hello@karengibbs.com.au
www.KarenGibbs.com.au

THE DEEPER PATH

I'm a certified coach of *The Deeper Path* by Kary Oberbrunner; it's a simple method for finding clarity, mastering life, and doing your purpose every day.

People who lose their way are people who've lost their *why*. It's time to start living from your true potential.

We all have potential, and we all have pain, but few people realise that when we numb our pain, we also numb our God-given potential. *The Deeper Path* leads you through your pain and into your potential. To go higher, you must first go deeper.

UNHACKABLE

The *Unhackable* message completely changed my life, and it can do the same for you.

Human knowledge once doubled every thousand years. Today, it's every twelve hours. No wonder we can't keep up. Advertising, cell phones, social media, multi-tasking, and constant disruptions are hacking our lives. Ditch the hype and tap into hope. It's time you created a life of focus and flow, where you feel your best and perform your best. Ask about my FREE book club. Thirty days, thirty missions to experience *Unhackability* in your life.

WOMEN'S CIRCLE OF HOPE AND HEALING

Women's Circle is a gathering of women in support of one another. Its purpose is to help every woman receive support and empowerment to live her own unique life to the fullest, just as God intended. This Circle experience is for all women, particularly those facing the effects of depression, anxiety, loss, or grief, either in themselves or in a loved one. Women's Circle is a fun, positive experience you won't want to miss.

    * Support *Transform *Discover * Shine in our women's group. Nurture yourself and others in this beautiful, shared experience.

    hello@karengibbs.com.au
    www.KarenGibbs.com.au

    Please note: I'm a certified Circle Facilitator, and in addition to working with women, I hold space for men, teens, bridal, and baby shower Circles. Please email for further details.

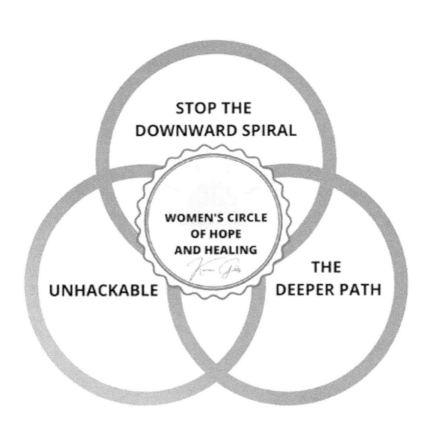

www.KarenGibbs.com.au

Future Hope

CHECK LIST

www.KarenGibbs.com.au

Join Stop The Downward
Spiral book club / coaching

Take the private assessment
on my web site

Discover "The Deeper Path"
coaching / study course

Experience "Unhackability"
FREE bookclub / coaching

Connect in Women's Circle
of Hope and Healing

Find support:
hello@karengibbs.com.au

https://karengibbs.com.au/

DISCUSSION QUESTION EXAMPLES

It's important not to trivialise depression or anxiety when discussing the symptoms with someone who is suffering. Holding space for them, being curious while showing concern, and showing loving support is the best way to proceed. Sometimes, your loved one will not want to talk, and that's fine too. Just being present without talking goes a long way to show you care, and more importantly, you understand. When your loved one feels connected, even in silence, it sometimes bridges the gap far better than a hundred questions ever could. Be comfortable in companionable silence.

If they want and need more support, open-ended questions cause a thought process that leads to breakthroughs. Listen with compassion to what your loved one has to say. If they are struggling and are willing to share, they want you to hear on a deep level. Acknowledge their feelings and show you're listening by repeating back some of what they are telling you. For example, *"So, you feel that . . ."* or *"It sounds like you . . ."* or *"What I'm hearing is . . ."* Showing you care by words and actions is never out of place but express it with empathy and concern, never judgement or panic. Keep calm at all times but seek urgent support if you feel there is a threat, e.g., suicidal ideation. Don't assume you can fix everything alone.

Depending on the person's symptoms and needs, here are basic examples of open-ended questions that might enlighten you. Using these examples, you can think of questions that pertain to the person's unique situation.

1. What's on your mind that is worrying you?
2. Do you feel your worry is a simple thing that you shouldn't be worried about, or is it something that needs further consideration?
3. How long have you had these worries, and have you asked anyone else to help you?

4. Do you experience physical symptoms such as higher heart rate or trembling when you think about these concerns?

5. Can you tell me more about your specific thoughts?

6. Does it concern you that you have these worrying thoughts? What can I do to better support you?

7. How long do you sleep without waking overnight, and is the pattern always the same?

8. Do you feel that your worrying contributes to a lack of sleep? Explain why.

9. How often are you bothered by feelings of anxiety or deep sadness?

10. Do you feel that your moods and your daily life are under your control? Explain why or why not.

11. Do you feel confident in your abilities to complete your daily tasks? If not, what do you think could be the cause?

12. What goals do you have that you are working toward actively?

13. What time frame do you expect to complete this, and can you do it alone?

14. Thinking about your support network, do you feel supported, and how does this make you feel?

15. What things are personally meaningful in your life, and how much time each day do you devote to these?

16. What other parts of your life do your worries affect?

17. Who else is affected by this problem?

18. Have you thought about any ideas that could alleviate the problem? If so, what are they?

19. Explain how you feel with your friends and family. Is there a deep connection to your loved ones?

20. Do you personally feel that you are understood? Why is that?

21. Name some people who you feel will be good support for you during this time.
22. What changes do you feel would improve your situation right now?
23. Can you name some ways to improve this situation?
24. What made you decide to seek help?
25. What strategies have you used to solve other problems in your life?

Never trivialise depression or anxiety and do NOT ask questions such as:

1. Don't you see how lucky you are?
2. Why do you make a big deal of everything?
3. Can't you pull yourself together?
4. Other people have it much worse than you. What have you got to be depressed about?
5. What's the matter with you, anyway?

These types of questions will make your loved one feel judged and misunderstood. This is not the outcome we are looking for. I wish you every success, and I believe in you. The fact that you care enough to read this book to the end shows that you can do this! Here's to a better life for all concerned.

From my heart to yours,
Karen xx

Disclaimer

Although the publisher and the author have made every effort to ensure that the information in this book was correct at press time and while this publication is designed to provide accurate information in regard to the subject matter covered, the publisher and the author assume no responsibility for errors, inaccuracies, omissions, or any other inconsistencies herein and hereby disclaim any liability to any party for any loss, damage, or disruption caused by errors or omissions, whether such errors or omissions result from negligence, accident, or any other cause.

This publication is meant as a source of valuable information for the reader; however it is not meant as a substitute for direct expert assistance. If such level of assistance is required, the services of a competent professional should be sought.

Notes

1   Beyond Blue. "What Causes Depression?" Accessed April 4, 2021. https://www.beyondblue.org.au/the-facts/depression/what-causes-depression.

2   American Psychiatric Association. "What Is Depression?" Accessed April 4, 2021. https://www.psychiatry.org/patients-families/depression/what-is-depression.

3   Anxiety & Depression Center. "Generalized Anxiety Disorder." Accessed April 6, 2021. https://anxietyanddepressioncenter.com/generalized-anxiety-disorder-newport-beach-ca/.

4   Anaïs Nin. *Seduction of the Minotaur.* Athens, OH: Swallow Press, 1961.

5   Joshua Wolf Shenk. "Lincoln's Great Depression." *The Atlantic.* October 2005. https://www.theatlantic.com/magazine/archive/2005/10/lincolns-great-depression/304247/.

6   Joshua Wolf Shenk. "Lincoln's Great Depression."

7   Joshua Wolf Shenk. "Lincoln's Great Depression."

8   Power of Positivity. "Jim Carrey's Beautiful Message for Anyone with Depression." July 11, 2019. https://www.powerofpositivity.com/jim-carrey-depression-message/.

9   Kaleem Aftab. "Jim Carrey: 'People have come at me and tried to break off a piece of the Holy Grail for themselves.'" *iNews.* November 23, 2017. https://inews.co.uk/essentials/jim-carrey-andy-and-jim-netflix-105397.

10   Power of Positivity. "Jim Carrey's Beautiful Message for Anyone with Depression."

11   LifeWorks AZ. "Depression Jim Carrey Actor Prozac Antidepressants." December 2008. http://www.lifeworksaz.com/counselors-blog/2008/12/depression-jim-carrey-actor-prozac/.

12   Johann Hari. *Lost Connections.* London: Bloomsbury, 2018.

13   National Institute of Mental Health. "Mental Health Medications." October 2016. https://www.nimh.nih.gov/health/topics/mental-health-medications/index.shtml.

14   Anil Rajvanshi. "How Three Minds of the Body—Brain, Heart, and Gut—Work Together for Producing Happiness." February 7, 2020. https://thriveglobal.com/stories/how-three-minds-of-the-body-brain-heart-and-gut-work-together-for-producing-happiness/.

15   Mladen Havelka, Jasminka Despot Lucanin, and Damir Damir Lucanin, "Biopsychosocial Model—the Integrated Approach to Health and Disease," *Collegium Antropologicum* 33, no. 1 (2009), https://pubmed.ncbi.nlm.nih.gov/19408642/.

16   Tim Cantopher. *Depressive Illness: The Curse of the Strong.* London: Sheldon Press, 2020.

17   Kary Oberbrunner. *The Deeper Path.* Powell, OH: Author Academy Elite, 2018.

18   Carlita Shaw. "Depression Is Not a Disease but an Indication That Human Consciousness Needs to Change." Voces Del Tierra. August 12, 2014. https://vocesdetierra.wordpress.com/2014/08/12/depression-is-not-a-disease-but-an-indication-that-human-consciousness-needs-to-change/.

Notes

19 *Wikipedia.* "Health of Abraham Lincoln." Accessed
    May 29, 2021. https://en.wikipedia.org/wiki/
    Health_of_Abraham_Lincoln.

20 Sue Mitchell. "COVID a 'sales changer' for supermarkets:
    Coles CEO." *Financial Review.* October 28, 2020. https://
    www.afr.com/companies/retail/coles-supermarket-liquor-sale
    s-buoyed-by-online-demand-20201027-p5695f.

21 Jill Newby. "Three Quarters of Australians Claim
    Their Mental Health Has Worsened by COVID-19."
    Black Dog Institute. Accessed May 29, 2020. https://
    www.blackdoginstitute.org.au/media-releases/
    three-quarters-of-australians-claim-their-mental-health-
    has-worsened-by-covid-19/.

22 Amy B. Wang. "Former Facebook VP Says Social Media
    Is Destroying Society with 'Dopamine-Driven Feedback
    Loops.'" *The Washington Post.* December 12, 2017. https://
    www.washingtonpost.com/news/the-switch/wp/2017/12/12/
    former-facebook-vp-says-social-media-is-destroying-society
    -with-dopamine-driven-feedback-loops/.

23 Jill Newby. "Three Quarters of Australians Claim Their
    Mental Health Has Worsened by COVID-19."

24 Ellen Ransley. "Annastacia Palaszczuk Says Queensland Is
    in for the Fight of Our Lives to Rebuild after Pandemic."
    The Weekend Australian. August 20, 2020. https://www.
    theaustralian.com.au/breaking-news/annastacia-palaszczu
    k-says-queensland-is-in-for-the-fight-of-
    our-lives-to-rebuild-after-pandemic/news-story/
    d53b77407ebf2462f661a151c8a494d8.

25 Ellen Ransley. "Annastacia Palaszczuk Says Queensland Is in
    for the Fight of Our Lives to Rebuild after Pandemic."

26 Maurizio Fava, MD. "Depression on the Rise During
    COVID-19: Resources for Patients and Their Families."
    Massachusetts General Hospital. June 25, 2020. https://www.
    massgeneral.org/news/coronavirus/depression-on-rise-durin
    g-covid-19.

27   Felix Richter. "Pandemic Causes Spike in Anxiety &
     Depression." Statista. January 18, 2021. https://www.
     statista.com/chart/21878/impact-of-coronavirus-pandemi
     c-on-mental-health/.

28   Joshua Wolf Shenk. "Lincoln's Great Depression."

29   GoodTherapy®. "What Is Melancholia?" September 19, 2018.
     https://www.goodtherapy.org/learn-about-therapy/issues/
     melancholia.

30   Lifeline. "Self-Harm." Accessed April 11, 2021. https://www.
     lifeline.org.au/get-help/information-and-support/self-harm/.

31   Maurizio Pompili, Gianluca Serafini, Marco Innamorati,
     Giovanni Dominici, Stefano Ferracuti, Giorgio D. Kotzalidis,
     Giulia Serra, et al. "Suicidal Behavior and Alcohol Abuse."
     *International Journal of Environmental Research and Public
     Health* 7, no. 4 (2010): 1392–1431. https://doi.org/10.3390/
     ijerph7041392.

32   BrainBiz. "The Neuroscience of Flow." Accessed April 11,
     2021. https://brainbiz.com.au/the-neuroscience-of-flow/.

33   Madeleine Burry. "Why Depression Makes You Tired and
     How to Deal with Fatigue." *Insider.* April 13, 2020. https://
     www.insider.com/why-does-depression-make-you-tired.

34   Charles P. O'Brien. "Neuroplasticity in Addictive Disorders."
     Dialogues in Clinical Neuroscience 11, no. 3 (2009): 350–353.
     https://dx.doi.org/10.31887/DCNS.2009.11.3/cpobrien.

35   Johns Hopkins Medicine. "The Brain-Gut Connection."
     Accessed April 15, 2021. https://www.hopkinsmedicine.org/
     health/wellness-and-prevention/the-brain-gut-connection.

36   Roger Segelken and Stacey Shackford. *Cornell Chronicle.* June
     10, 2014. https://news.cornell.edu/stories/2014/06/news-fee
     d-emotional-contagion-sweeps-facebook.

37   John Rampton. "Neuroscience Tells Us How to Hack Our
     Brains for Success." *Entrepreneur.* June 16, 2017. https://www.
     entrepreneur.com/article/295885.

38   Dr. Samantha Rodman. "6 Reasons Why It's Hard for People
     with Depression to Exercise." Talkspace. January 4, 2018.

https://www.talkspace.com/blog/6-reasons-why-its-hard-fo
r-people-with-depression-to-exercise/.

39   Charles Duhigg. *The Power of Habit.* New York: Random
House, 2012.

40   Kary Oberbrunner. *Unhackable.* Powell, OH: Ethos
Collective, 2020.

41   Bruce K. Alexander. "Addiction: The View from Rat Park."
2010. https://www.brucekalexander.com/articles-speeches/
rat-park/148-addiction-the-view-from-rat-park.

42   Bruce K. Alexander. "Addiction: The View from Rat Park."

43   Tom Stafford. "Drug Addiction: The Complex Truth."
BBC. September 9, 2013. https://www.bbc.com/future/articl
e/20130910-drug-addiction-the-complex-truth.

44   Lee N. Robins, Darlene H. Davis, and David N. Nurco. "How
Permanent Was Vietnam Drug Addiction?" *American Journal
of Public Health* 64, no. 12_Suppl (1974): 38–43. https://doi.
org/10.2105/ajph.64.12_suppl.38.

45   Bill Hoffman. "Now That's a Barramundi! Matt's
Biggest Catch Yet." *Sunshine Coast Daily.* February 6,
2014. https://www.sunshinecoastdaily.com.au/news/
what-a-catch-matt/2161906/.

CPSIA information can be obtained
at www.ICGtesting.com
Printed in the USA
BVHW041650200821
614848BV00014B/241